CHALLENGING TRAVEL PUZZLES

THIS IS A CARLTON BOOK

This edition published in 2018
by Carlton Books Limited
20 Mortimer Street
London W1T 3JW

ISBN: 978-1-78739-099-7

Text and puzzles in this edition first appeared in:
Mensa Family Quiz Book
Mensa Mighty Mind Mazes
Mensa Ultimate Mental Challenge

Printed and bound in Great Britain by CPI Group (UK) Ltd, Croydon CR0 4YY

10 9 8 7 6 5 4 3 2 1

CHALLENGING TRAVEL PUZZLES

Problems to broaden your mind wherever you are

What is Mensa?

Mensa is the international society for people with a high IQ. Today there are around 110,000 Mensans in 100 countries throughout the world. There are active Mensa organizations in more than 40 countries.

The society's aims are:

- to identify and foster human intelligence for the benefit of humanity
- to encourage research in the nature, characteristics, and uses of intelligence
- to provide a stimulating intellectual and social environment for its members

Anyone with an IQ score in the top two per cent of population is eligible to become a member of Mensa – are you the 'one in 50' we've been looking for?

Mensa membership offers an excellent range of benefits:

- Networking and social activities nationally and around the world
- Special Interest Groups – hundreds of chances to pursue your hobbies and interests – from art to zoology!
- Monthly members' magazine and regional newsletters
- Local meetings – from games challenges to food and drink
- National and international weekend gatherings and conferences
- Intellectually stimulating lectures and seminars
- Access to the worldwide SIGHT network for travellers and hosts

For more information about Mensa: www.mensa.org/about-us, or

British Mensa Ltd.,
St John's House,
St John's Square,
Wolverhampton
WV2 4AH
Telephone: +44 (0) 1902 772771
E-mail: enquiries@mensa.org.uk
www.mensa.org.uk

CONTENTS

Welcome, puzzle-lover!

This book contains a selection of puzzles to give your brain a workout, even when you're on the move.
You don't have to work your way through the book from start to finish. If you feel like doing the quizzes first, or all of the number puzzles in one go, feel free – the order is up to you. There's only one exception – the Mind Maze should be completed in one go, because the answers all add up to a big, final solution.

Good luck, and happy puzzling on your travels!

1 Which state is known as the 'Bluegrass State'?

2 Which is the smallest state?

3 Which river does the Ohio flow into?

4 In which year was the Constitution drawn up?

5 Which is the legislative branch of the federal government?

6 How many colonies declared their independence from Britain in 1776?

7 Which state has the highest population?

8 Which was the first permanent European settlement in the present USA?

9 Who was the seventh president?

10 Which two houses make up the Congress?

11 Which are the three largest cities in the country?

12 What is the capital of Florida?

13 Which war took place between 1835 and 1842?

14 In which part of the country do Apaches now live?

15 Which event precipitated the Mexican War?

16 What is the name given to the 11 southern states that seceded from the USA in 1860?

17 Which political party did Theodore Roosevelt stand for?

18 What is the maximum term for a US president?

19 What is the minimum age for someone to become president?

20 What is the capital of Maine?

21 Who succeeded President John F. Kennedy?

22 Which west-coast state forms its northern border with Canada?

23 What was the name of the independent candidate in the 1992 presidential election?

24 What is the name given to the domestic reform program of President Roosevelt during the Great Depression?

25 On which river is Washington D.C. situated?

26 Which festival is celebrated in New Orleans on Shrove Tuesday?

27 What is the name of the national anthem?

28 What is the capital of Alaska?

29 Geronimo was the leader of which tribe?

30 On which river is Memphis situated?

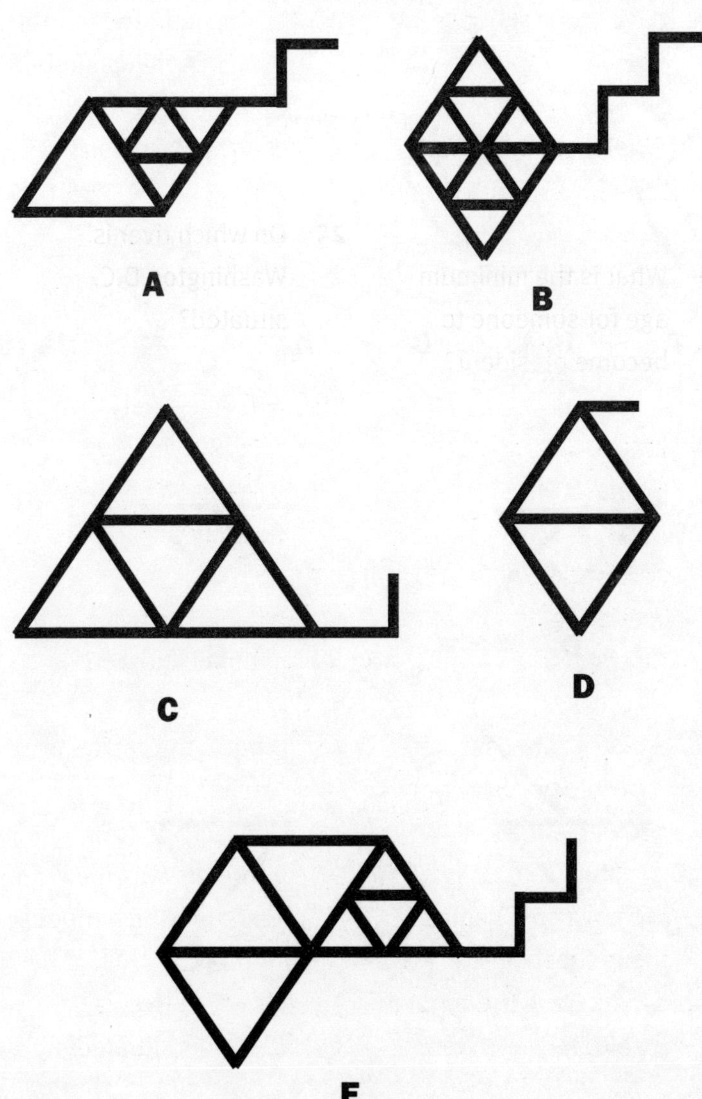
A
B
C
D
E

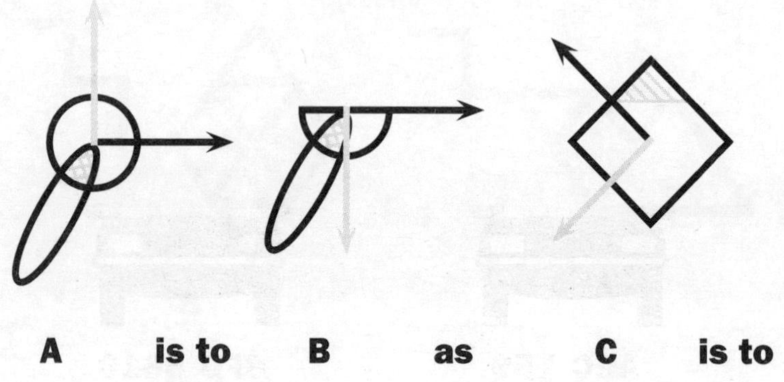
A is to B as C is to

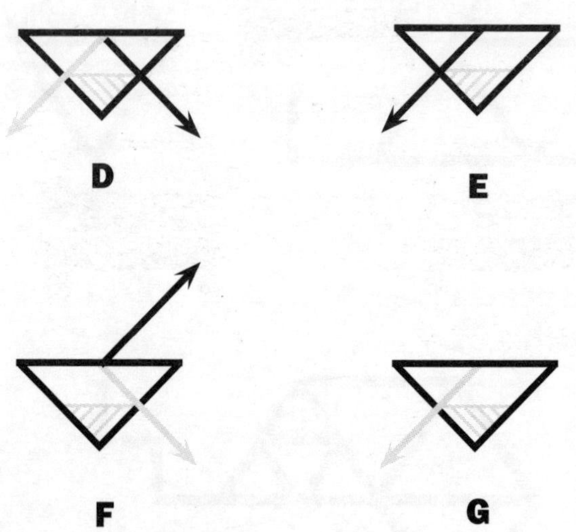
D
E
F
G

The registration plates of all these cars conform to a certain logic. Can you work out the final plate?

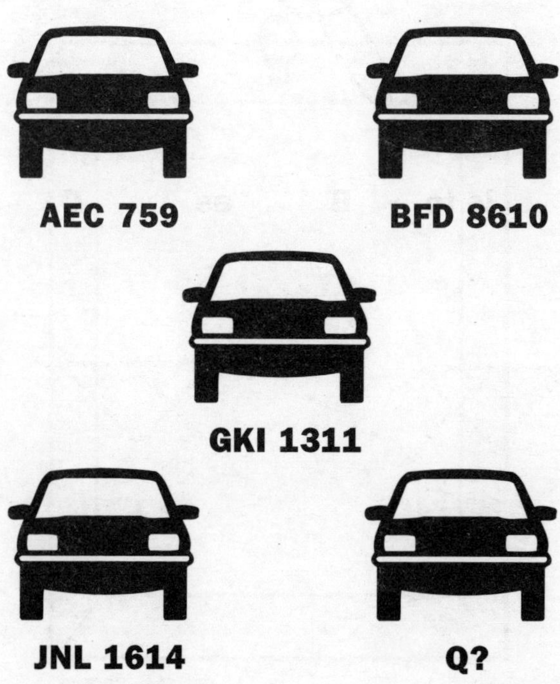

FIND THE ARTIST

Can you unravel the code on the back of the picture to find the name of its artist?

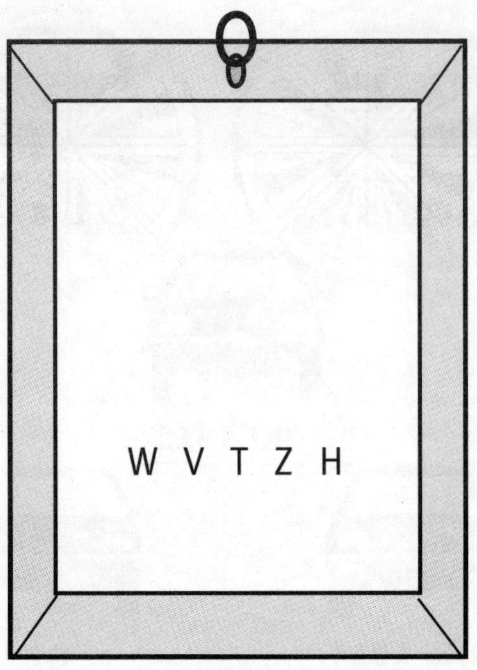

Can you work out what the missing section in the last wheel should look like?

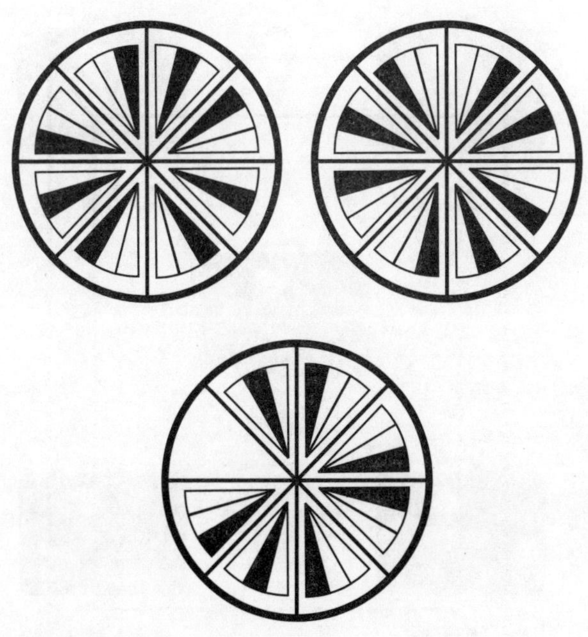

ODD-ONE-OUT

PUZZLE 7

The weight of each suitcase is shown. Which is the odd one out?

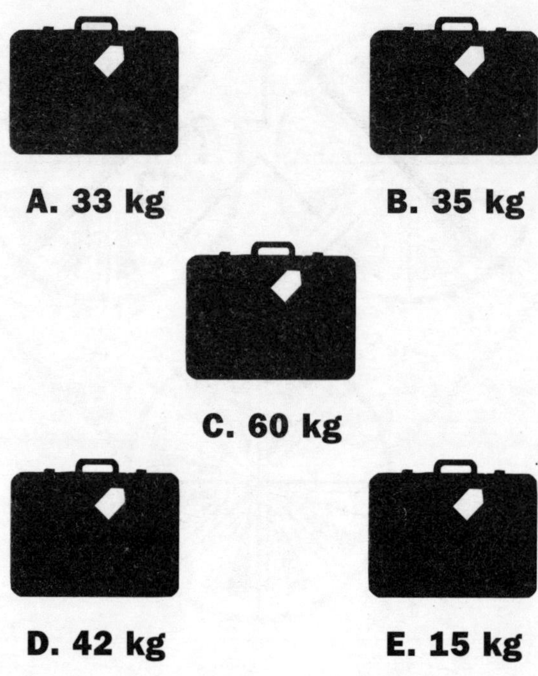

In this diagram the four basic mathematical signs (+, –, x, ÷) have been missed out. Can you replace the question marks?

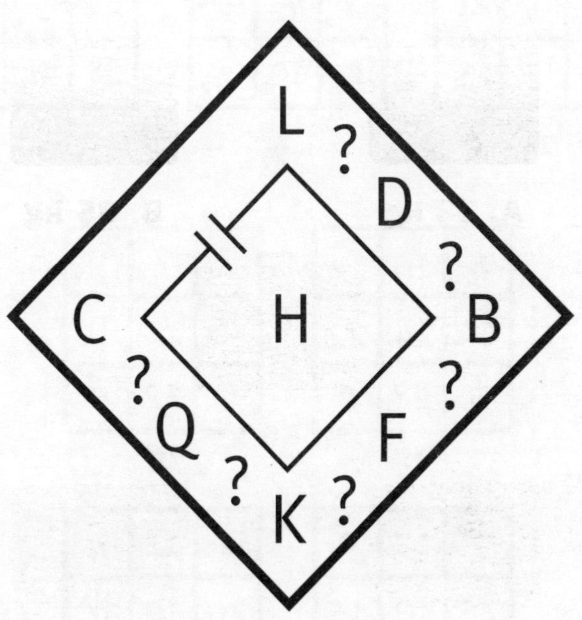

5	6	9
4	3	2
0	7	1

8	4	12
2	6	0
0	10	4

4	9	6
22	7	11
2	14	1

A is to B as C is to

8	18	12
44	14	22
4	28	2

D

7	7	9
25	5	9
5	17	0

E

7	12	9
25	10	14
5	17	4

F

2	12	4
20	10	14
0	12	4

G

Take one letter from each bulb in order. You should be able to make five five-letter words related to food.

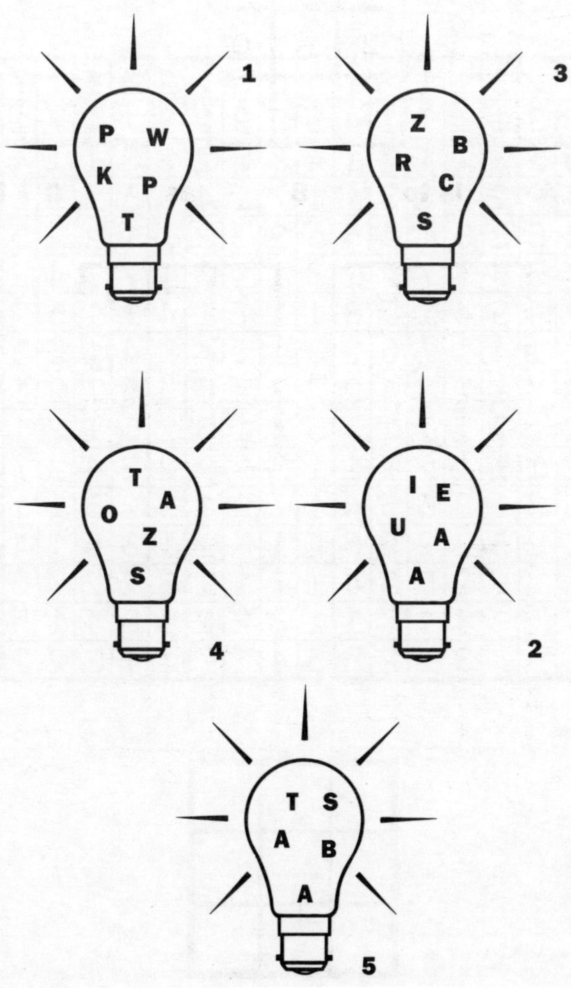

Can you work out the reasoning behind this grid and complete the missing section?

2	2	3	1	1	7	1	4	5	5	2	2	3	1	1	7
5	3	1	1	7	1	4	5	5	2	2	3	1	1	7	1
5	2	3	1	1	7	1	4	5	5	2	2	3	1	1	4
4	2	2	2	2	3	1	1	7	1	4	5	5	2	7	5
1	5	2	5	1	4	5	5	2	2	3	1	1	2	1	5
7	5	5	5	7	2	2	3	1	1	7	1	7	3	4	2
1	4	5	4	1	5	3	1	1	7	1	4	1	1	5	2
1	1	4	1	1	5	2	3	1	1	4	5	4	1	5	3
3	7	1	7	3	4	2	2	2	7	5	5	5	7	2	1
2	1	7	1	2	1	5	5	4	1	5	2	5	1	2	1
2	1	1	1	2	7	1	1	3	2	2	2	2	4	3	7
5	3	1	3	5	5	4	1	7	1	1	3	2	5	1	1
5	2	3	2	2	5	5	4	1	7	1	1	3	5	1	4
			2	5	5	4	1	7	1	1	3	2	2	7	5
			4	1	7	1	1	3	2	2	5	5	4	1	5
			3	2	2	5	5	4	1	7	1	1	3	2	2

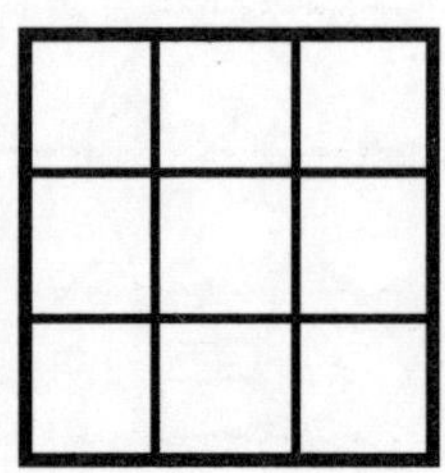

Can you work out the pattern sequence and fill in the missing section?

&	&	%	*	%	@	@	%	*	&	&	%	*	%	@	@
*	@	@	%	*	&	&	%	*	%	@	@	%	*	&	&
%	%	&	&	%	*	%	@	@	%	*	&	&	%	*	%
@	*	*	*	%	@	@	%	*	&	&	%	*	%	%	*
@	%	%	%	@				&	&	%	*	%	@	@	%
%	&	@	&	%				&	&	%	*	@	@	@	@
*	&	@	&	*				*	&	&	%	@	%	%	@
%	*	%	*	%	%	@	@	@	%	%	@	%	*	*	%
&	%	*	%	&	*	%	%	*	*	*	@	*	&	&	*
&	@	%	@	&	%	*	%	&	&	%	%	&	&	&	&
*	@	&	@	*	&	&	*	%	@	@	*	&	%	%	&
%	%	&	%	%	@	@	%	*	%	&	&	%	*	*	%
@	*	*	*	%	&	&	*	%	@	@	%	*	%	%	*
@	%	%	@	@	%	*	%	&	&	*	%	@	@	@	%
%	&	&	*	%	@	@	%	*	%	&	&	*	%	@	@
*	%	&	&	*	%	@	@	%	*	%	&	&	*	%	@

Can you find the missing number in this square?

1536	48	96	3
384	192	24	12
768	96	48	6
192	?	12	24

1 Who wrote the novel From Russia With Love?

2 What is the name of Rome's airport?

3 Which US political party has the donkey as its symbol?

4 In Rome, which flight of 137 stairs leads from Piazza di Spagne to the Church of the Trinita dei Monti?

5 With which sport do you associate Imran Khan?

6 Name the woman who was prime minister of Pakistan twice.

7 Of which political party was Zhou Enlai a leader?

8 How, in olden days, did the Chinese most commonly refer to their country?

9 The name of the Australian airline QANTAS is an acronym. What does it stand for?

10 Which is the largest lake in Africa?

11 To which country does the word Singhalese refer?

12 In Asian countries, the word 'singh' is commonly used. What does it mean?

13 In which subcontinent would you hear Urdu, Hindi, and Bengali spoken as native languages?

14 Which English university city stands on the river Cam?

15 Cellist Jacqueline du Pré died of which illness?

16 Who wrote Far From the Madding Crowd?

17 Which organs of the body produce urine?

18 What substance is produced by the gall bladder?

19 What boon to gardeners was invented by Mr Budding and Mr Ferrabee?

20 Why is a mausoleum so-called?

21 What were the pre-communist rulers of Russia called?

22 What, in military terms, is a SAM?

23 Which country is the home of the Sony electronics company?

24 Which US poet broadcast Fascist propaganda during World War II?

25 What is the more formal name of London's Old Bailey?

26 Who shot John Lennon?

27 Who tried to assassinate President Ford in Sacramento?

28 Which US president withdrew US forces from Vietnam?

29 What is a locum?

30 What is the charleston?

31 Edward VIII of England abdicated to marry an American divorcee. What was her name?

32 Of which country is Vientiane the capital?

33 In which country would you find political parties called Fianna Fail and Fine Gael?

34 Which literary character made famous the phrase, 'Tomorrow is another day'?

35 What other name is used for the Erse language?

36 Who wrote *Catch-22*?

37 In which year did the Six Day War take place?

38 Was Munich in East or West Germany?

39 Which fictional character would have made you an offer you could not refuse?

40 Whose house was moved by Pooh and Piglet?

41 What is an obsequy?

42 Who was the last woman to be hanged in Britain?

43 In which year was the Panama Canal completed?

44 What sort of music do you associate with Nashville, Tennessee?

45 Who wrote *For Whom the Bell Tolls*?

46 What is the connection between Truman Capote, Audrey Hepburn, and a morning meal?

47 How often are the Olympic Games held?

48 A funeral director is called different things in British and American English. Can you give both versions?

49 In English, we use the French phrase cul de sac to mean a street closed at one end. Why is the phrase not used in France?

50 What was tennis star Evonne Cawley's maiden name?

Can you work out which of these musical terms is the odd one out?

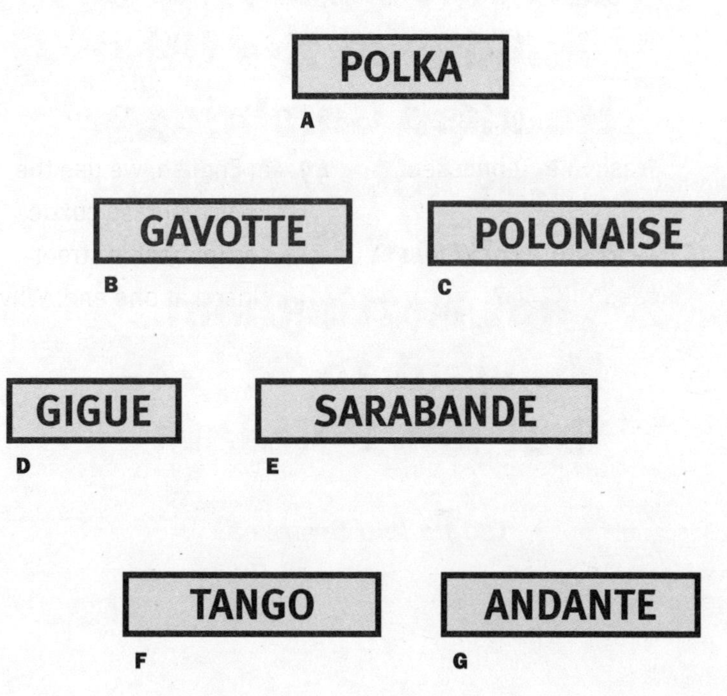

Earl left Dallas for a holiday in the UK. He liked Cambridge but not Oxford. He visited Derby but not Nottingham. He went to St Ives but not Polzeath.

Did he like Swansea?

FIND THE LETTER

PUZZLE 17

Can you work out which letter should replace the question mark?

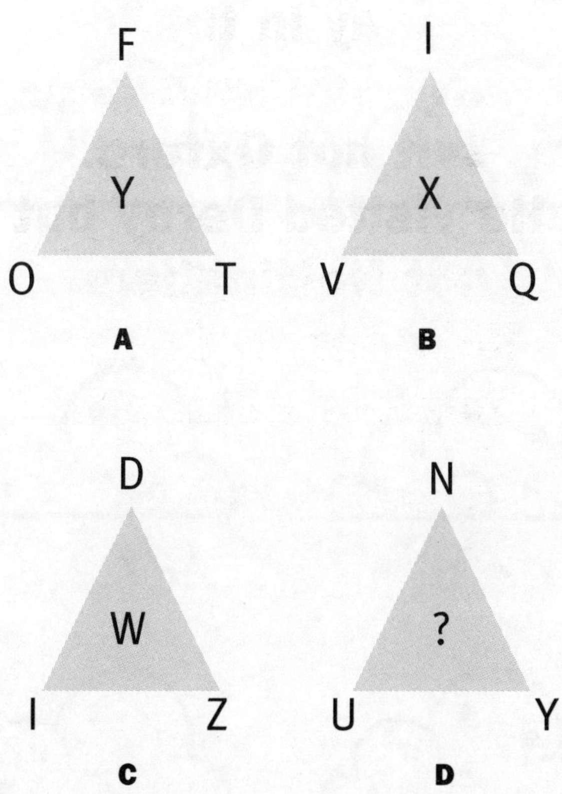

Take one letter from each cloud in order. You should be able to make five foreign words that have entered the English language.

These trains pass three American towns on their route. Can you find the missing town of the last train?

a) Baltimore
b) Fresno
c) Boston
d) Philadelphia

A

Albuquerque
Denver
Grand Island

B

Minneapolis
Portland
San Diego

C

Pueblo
Sacramento
Victoria

D

Buffalo
Evansville
Hannibal

E

Clearwater
—?—
Indianapolis

Can you work out which triangle does not follow the same rule as the others?

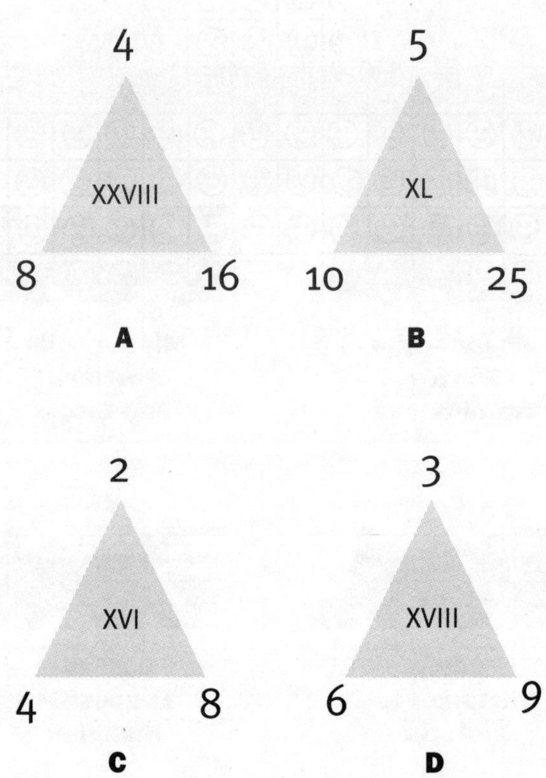

COMPLETE THE SECTION

PUZZLE 21

This grid is made up according to a certain pattern. Can you work it out and fill in the missing section?

🙁	😐	🙂	🙂	🙁	😐	😐	🙂	🙁	🙁	😐	🙂	🙂	🙁	😐	😐
🙁	🙂	🙂	😐	🙁	🙁	🙂	😐	😐	🙁	🙂	🙂	😐	🙁	🙁	🙂
😐	😐	🙂	🙁	🙁	😐	🙂	🙂	🙁	😐	😐	🙂	🙁	🙁	😐	🙂
🙁	🙁	🙂	😐	😐	🙁	🙂	🙂	😐	🙁	🙁	🙂	😐	😐	🙁	🙂
😐	🙂	🙂	🙁	😐	😐	🙂	🙁	🙁	😐	🙂	🙂	🙁	😐	😐	🙂
😐	🙁	🙂	🙂	😐	🙁	🙁	🙂	😐	😐	🙁	🙂	🙂	😐	🙁	🙁
😐	🙂	🙁	🙁	😐	🙂	🙂	🙁	😐	😐	🙂	🙁	🙁	😐	🙂	🙂
😐	🙁	🙁	🙂	😐	😐	🙁	🙂	🙂	😐	🙁	🙁	🙂	😐	😐	🙁
🙂	🙂	🙁	😐	😐	🙂	🙁	🙁				🙁	😐	😐	🙂	🙁
😐	😐	🙁	🙂	🙂	😐	🙁	🙁				🙁	🙂	🙂	😐	🙁
🙂	🙁	🙁	😐	🙂	🙂	🙁	😐				🙁	😐	🙂	🙂	🙁
🙂	😐	🙁	🙁	🙂	😐	😐	🙁	🙂	🙂	😐	🙁	🙁	🙂	😐	😐
🙂	🙁	😐	😐	🙂	🙁	🙁	😐	🙂	🙂	🙁	😐	😐	🙂	🙁	🙁
🙂	😐	😐	🙁	🙂	🙂	😐	🙁	🙁	🙂	😐	😐	🙁	🙂	🙂	😐
🙁	🙁	😐	🙂	🙂	🙁	😐	😐	🙂	🙁	🙁	😐	🙂	🙂	🙁	😐
🙂	🙂	😐	🙁	🙁	🙂	😐	😐	🙁	🙂	🙂	😐	🙁	🙁	🙂	😐

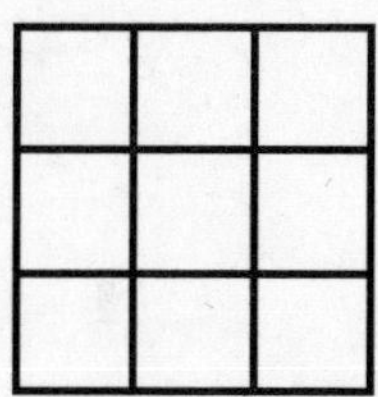

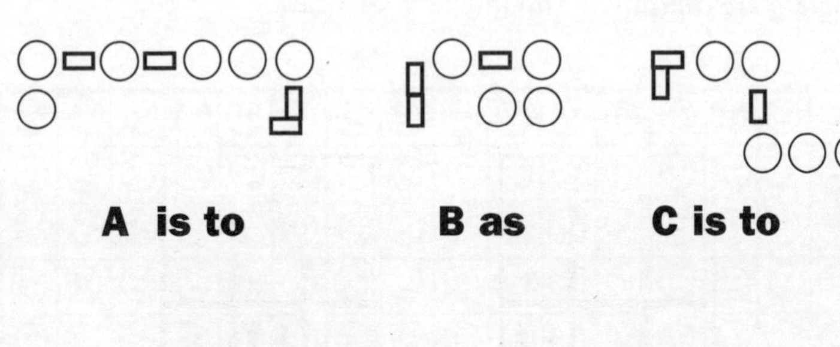
A is to
B as
C is to

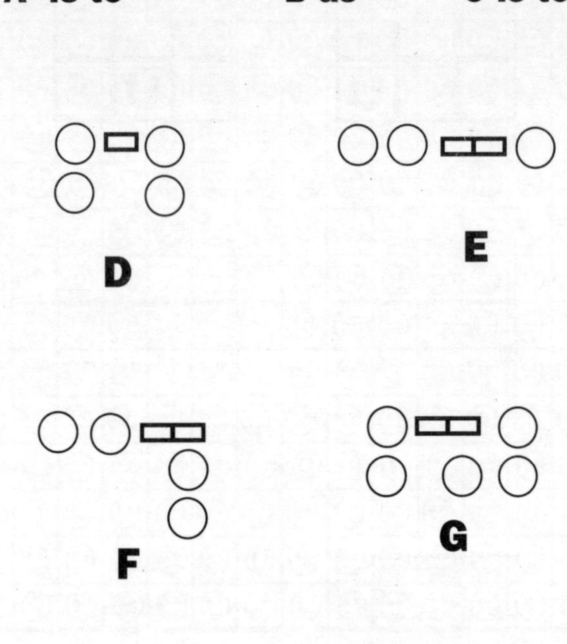
D
E
F
G

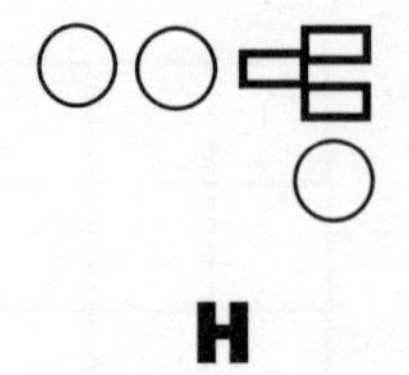
H

Can you work out what the next grid in this sequence should look like?

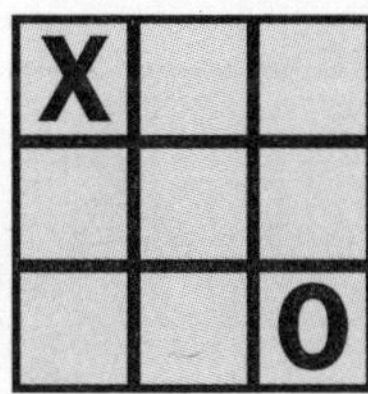
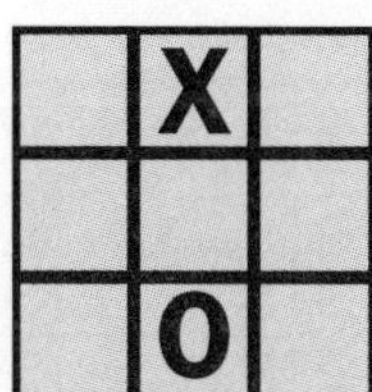
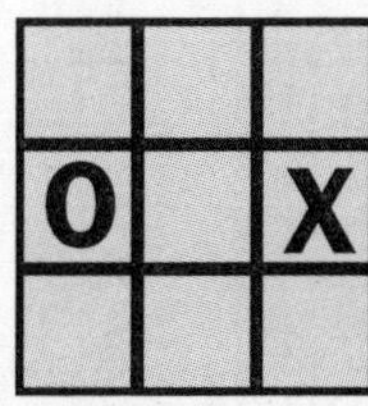
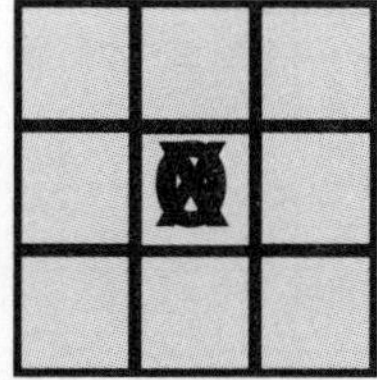
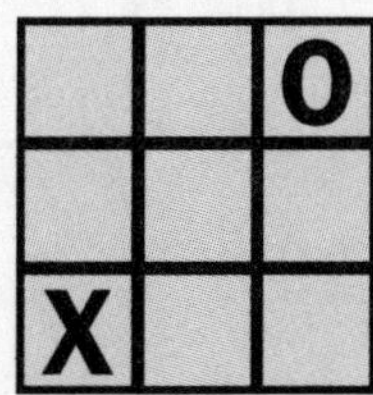

The word SERPENTINE is hidden somewhere in this grid. It occurs in its entirety only once. Can you find it? It may be spelt in any direction but is all in one line.

S	E	R	E	P	E	N	S	T	I	N	E	R	E	S	E
E	E	S	E	N	R	P	E	N	S	E	R	P	E	N	T
R	S	R	S	E	I	S	R	T	E	R	P	E	N	T	I
P	E	P	P	S	E	T	P	I	N	E	N	E	S	S	S
E	R	E	S	N	T	N	N	N	E	R	I	N	N	N	E
N	P	N	E	R	T	E	T	E	P	N	S	E	E	I	R
T	E	T	R	P	S	I	I	T	P	T	P	T	R	T	P
N	N	I	P	E	E	N	N	T	R	R	S	E	P	N	E
E	T	N	E	N	T	E	E	E	E	S	E	T	E	E	N
I	N	E	N	T	R	S	E	S	R	E	T	S	N	P	T
S	E	R	T	P	E	N	T	I	N	E	T	S	T	R	I
S	E	R	N	P	E	N	T	I	N	E	E	N	I	E	T
E	S	R	E	I	S	E	R	P	E	N	T	I	N	S	E
S	E	T	E	N	N	I	T	N	E	P	R	E	S	T	E
R	S	E	N	E	I	T	N	I	P	R	E	S	E	S	T
S	E	R	P	E	N	S	N	I	T	N	E	P	R	E	S

Each balloon has been sponsored by a famous newspaper. The number is somehow linked to the paper's name. What is the number of *The Independent's* balloon?

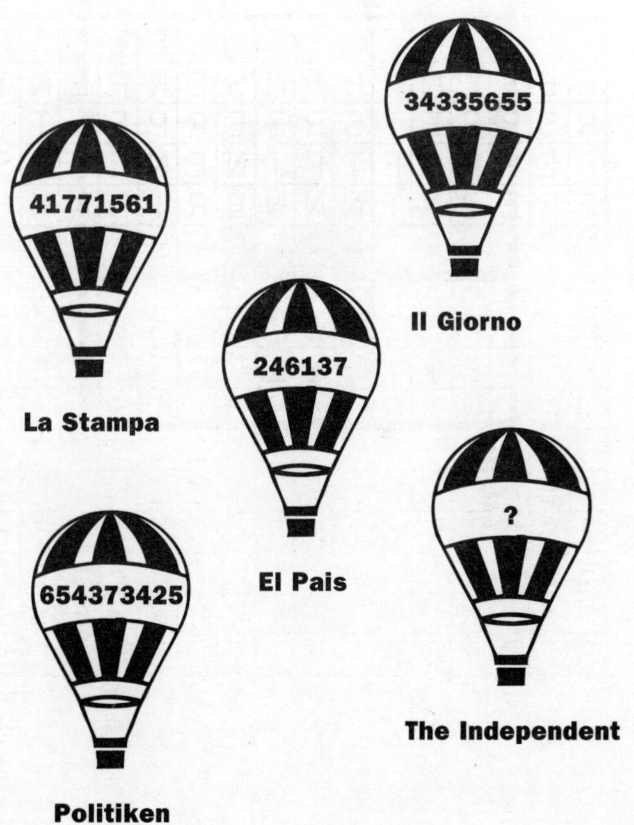

Can you work out the logic behind this square and find the missing number?

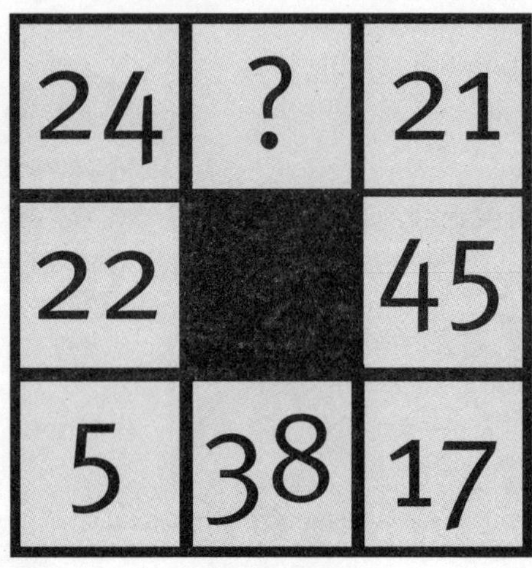

24	?	21
22		45
5	38	17

1 What is an aubergine (eggplant) parmigiana topped with?

2 What type of vegetable is a capsicum?

3 What is rutabaga also known as?

4 What is sushi traditionally wrapped in?

5 What type of fish is scampi?

6 Where does marsala originate from?

7 What type of food is Monterey Jack?

8 Name the cold dessert of stewed or puréed fruit mixed with cream or custard.

9 What is sake made from?

10 Which type of pepper is used as a stuffing for green olives?

11 What do you call a dish of ice-cream with a topping of nuts, sauce, or whipped cream?

12 What is a vol-au-vent usually filled with?

13 What is mayonnaise made of?

14 What is a blancmange?

15 What type of sauce would a chicken à la king be cooked in?

16 What is an alligator pear also known as?

17 What is whisky made from?

18 Which spice is sambal seasoned with?

19 What type of alcohol does a pink lady contain?

20 What type of dairy product does beef stroganoff contain?

21 What type of food is a shiitake?

22 What type of seed is mace made from?

23 To make a Scotch egg, what is the egg wrapped in?

24 What is a meringue made of?

25 What is aquavit flavoured with?

26 What type of food is a madeleine?

27 To make beef Wellington, what is the beef covered with?

28 What type of cake is a strudel?

29 If you sauté potatoes, how do you cook them?

30 What is the main ingredient of a guacamole?

31 What is curaçao flavoured with?

32 What type of food is a pirog?

33 What is the name for a white sauce made with butter, flour, and milk or cream?

34 What is piccalilli?

35 What is a pina colada made of?

36 Which country does Limburger cheese come from?

37 What do you call the fragrance of a wine or liqueur?

38 What does the word 'florentine' after a dish imply?

39 Which herbs is Béarnaise sauce flavoured with?

40 What type of dish is chicken jalfrezi?

41 What is carob used as a substitute for?

42 What is crème de cassis made from?

43 Where does the dish teriyaki come from?

44 Which sauce are eggs Benedict topped with?

45 What do you call a mixture of flour and fat cooked together, usually as a base for sauces?

46 What sort of drink is manzanilla?

47 What part of the animal does sweetbread come from?

48 In what type of cooking would you use hoisin sauce?

49 What type of sauce is a satay usually dipped in?

50 Which part of the pig are chitterlings?

Can you find the letter that comes next in this series?

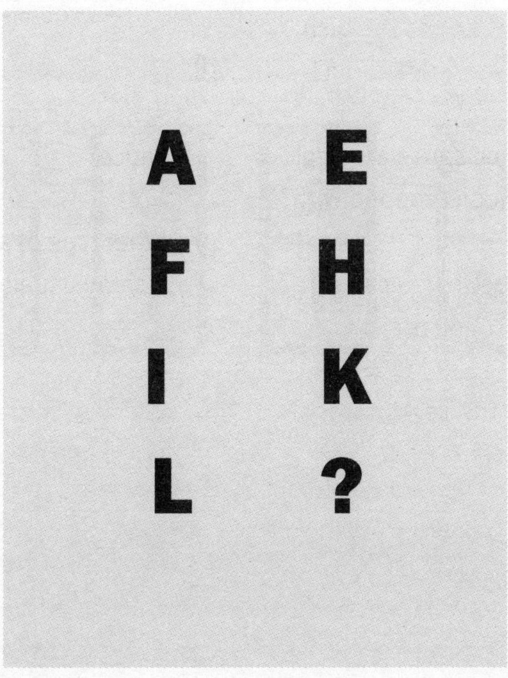

Can you unravel the logic behind these domino pieces and fill in the missing letter?

COMPLETE THE SECTION

PUZZLE 30

Can you spot the pattern of this grid and complete the missing section?

Z	R	T	T	U	W	W	Z	Z	S	Z	R	T	T	U	W
S	Z	Z	W	W	U	T	T	R	Z	S	Z	Z	W	W	U
Z	S	Z	R	T	T	U	W	W	Z	Z	S	Z	R	T	T
Z	W	W	U	T	T	R	Z	S	Z	Z	W	W	U	T	T
W	Z	Z	S	Z	R	T	T				Z	Z	S	Z	R
W	U	T	T	R	Z	S	Z				U	T	T	R	Z
U	W	W	Z	Z	S	Z	R				W	W	Z	Z	S
T	T	R	Z	S	Z	Z	W	W	U	T	T	R	Z	S	Z
T	T	U	W	W	Z	Z	S	Z	R	T	T	U	W	W	Z
R	Z	S	Z	Z	W	W	U	T	T	R	Z	S	Z	Z	W
Z	R	T	T	U	W	W	Z	Z	S	Z	R	T	T	U	W
S	Z	Z	W	W	U	T	T	R	Z	S	Z	Z	W	W	U
Z	S	Z	R	T	T	U	W	W	Z	Z	S	Z	R	T	T
Z	W	W	U	T	T	R	Z	S	Z	Z	W	W	U	T	T
W	Z	Z	S	Z	R	T	T	U	W	W	Z	Z	S	Z	R
W	U	T	T	R	Z	S	Z	Z	W	W	U	T	T	R	Z

Which of these layouts could be used to make this cube?

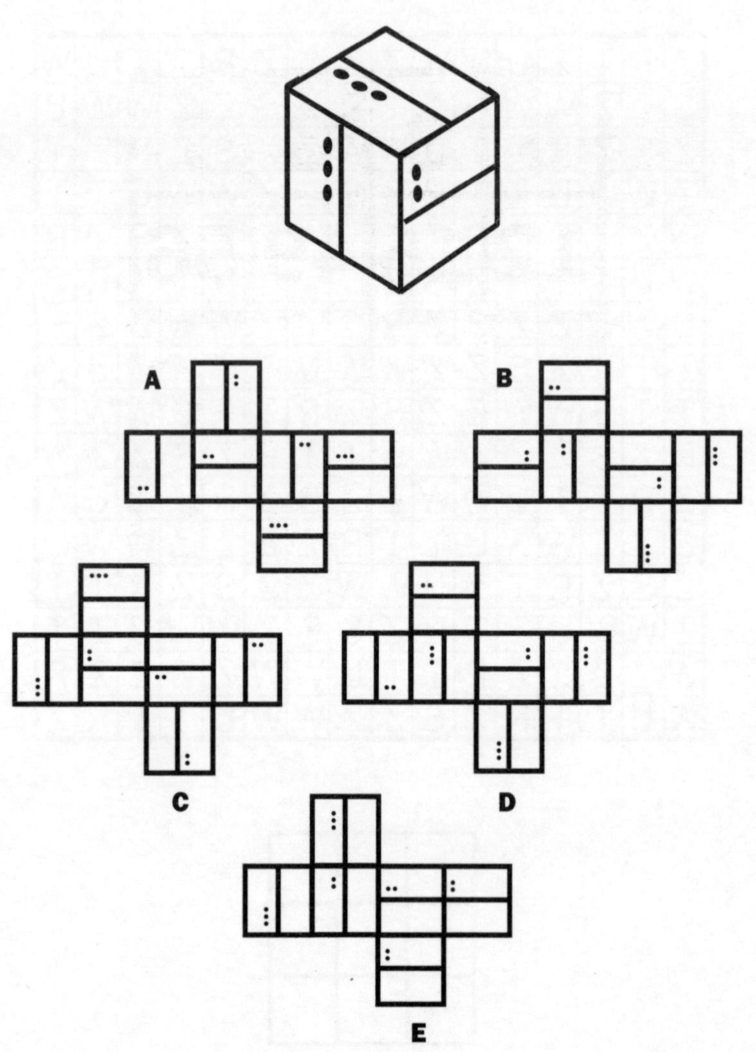

FIND THE NUMBER — PUZZLE 32

Can you work out the reasoning behind this square and replace the question mark with a number?

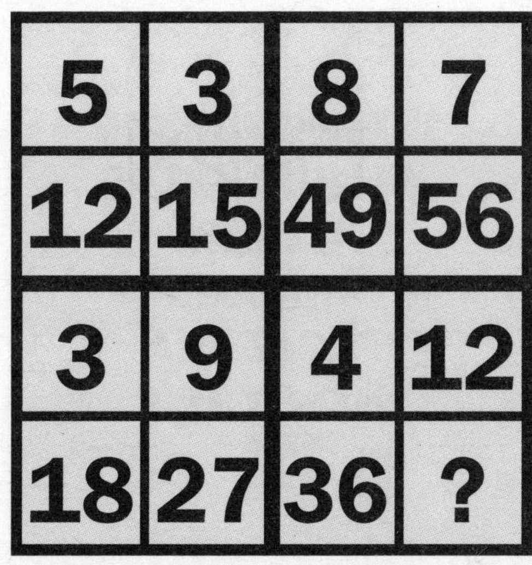

5	3	8	7
12	15	49	56
3	9	4	12
18	27	36	?

Which of the names in the top panel can be added to the ones in the bottom? This may seem confusing initially but, despite appearances, it is not an American puzzle and you will find a capital solution.

INDEPENDENCE
WICHITA FALLS
ATLANTA
CHICAGO
PASADENA
NEW YORK

MINNEAPOLIS
DALLAS
ANDOVER
ROCKFORD
DAVENPORT

Stephie goes on holiday around Europe.
She likes Hamburg but hates Berlin.
She likes Strasbourg but avoids Paris.
She loves Barcelona but hates Madrid.

Does she like London?

Pick one letter from each cloud in order. You should be able to make the names of five Roman emperors.

This grid follows a certain pattern. Can you work out which signs complete the missing grid?

+	+	−	−	−	÷	÷	X	X	X	+	+	−	−	−	÷
X	+	+	−	−	−	÷	÷	X	X	X	+	+	−	−	÷
X	+	−	−	−	÷	÷	X	X	X	+	+	−	−	−	X
X	+	÷	÷	X	X	X	+	+	−	−	−	÷	−	÷	X
÷	X	−	+	−	−	−	÷	÷	X	X	X	÷	÷	÷	X
÷	X	−	+	X	+	+	−	−	−	÷	+	X	÷	X	+
−	X	−	X	X	X	+	+	−	−	÷	+	X	X	X	+
−	÷	+	X	X	X	+	−	−	−	X	−	X	X	X	−
−	÷	+	X	÷				−	÷	X	−	+	X	+	−
+	−	X	÷	÷				X	÷	X	−	+	+	+	−
+	−	X	÷	−				−	+	+	÷	−	+	−	÷
X	−	X	−	−	−	+	+	X	X	X	÷	−	−	−	÷
X	+	÷	−	−	+	+	X	X	X	÷	÷	−	−	−	X
X	+	÷	−	−	−	+	+	X	X	X	÷	÷	−	÷	X
÷	X	X	X	÷	÷	−	−	−	+	+	X	X	X	÷	X
÷	−	−	−	+	+	X	X	X	÷	÷	−	−	−	+	+

Can you work out where the shaded square in the last diagram should be?

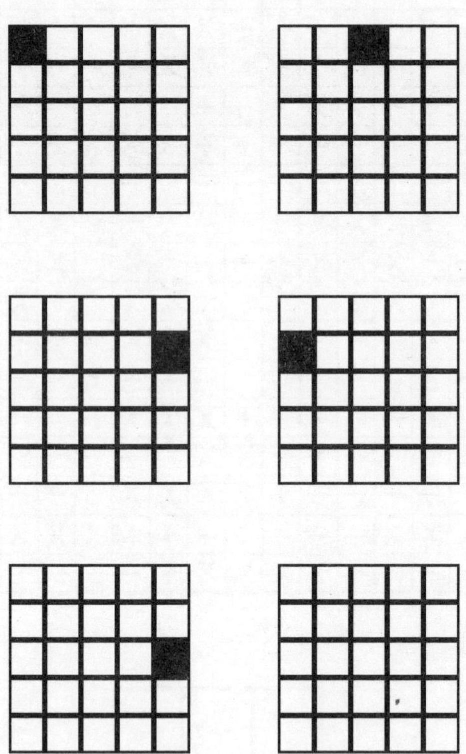

Can you work out the reasoning behind these squares and replace the question mark with a number?

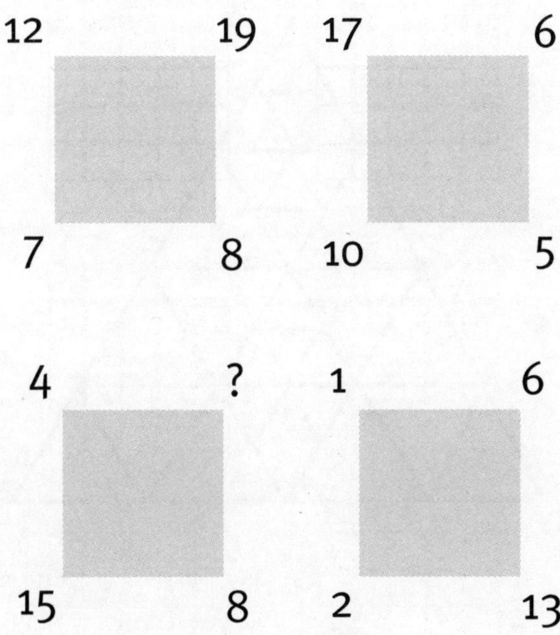

Can you work out how many triangles there are altogether in this diagram?

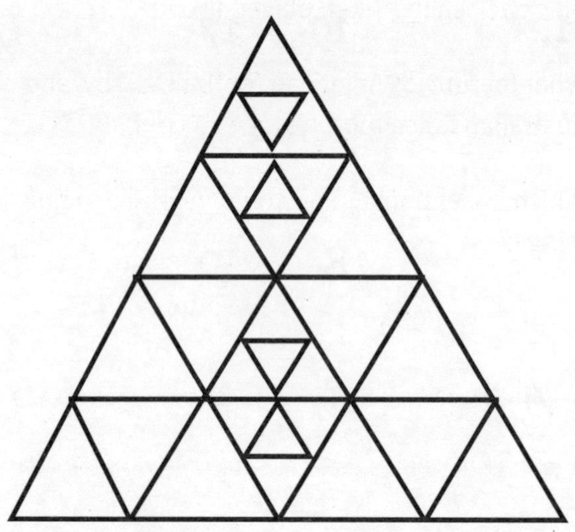

1 Which side moves first in a game of chess?

2 By what name is Hsiang Ch'i known in the west?

3 What is the casino game of Blackjack called when played for fun?

4 What feature do American football, rugby, and Australian Rules football have in common?

5 Which boxer boasted he could 'float like a butterfly and sting like a bee'?

6 In which game can you 'huff'?

7 In which game might you capture a piece 'en passant'?

8 Which cousin of snooker and pool uses only three balls?

9 In which game might you play a 'full house'?

10 In which sport might you occupy the position of 'silly mid on'?

11 In which sport would you hope to score a strike?

12 In which sport would you try to avoid three strikes?

13 What name is given to the pitch on which American football is played?

14 In which game is the ball thrown with the aid of a large wicker scoop worn on the hand?

15 In which sport might you use ashi-waza?

16 In American football, what is the maximum number of men who can play for each team during a single match?

17 What is the name of the 'human spider' that forms such an important part of a rugby match?

18 Rugby balls used to be made of camelskin. True or false?

19 Which very dangerous Native American game, once known as 'the little brother of war', is now played mainly by women?

20 Which is the fastest team sport in the world?

21 What is the popular name for the place where ice hockey players are sent for breaking the rules?

22 Which popular game was invented by a Canadian clergyman using two peach baskets?

23 How many players are there in a netball team?

24 In which sport is a ball knocked back and forth across a net by hand?

25 Joe DiMaggio was a legendary player of which sport?

26 Are aluminium bats allowed in Major League baseball?

27 In baseball, spiked boots are not allowed. What are used instead?

28 In cricket, what is a sequence of six or eight balls called?

29 From what wood are cricket bats traditionally made?

30 What form of tennis was once the sport of kings?

31 The French game of Jeu de Paume was the precursor of what modern sport?

32 In which century was lawn tennis first played?

33 Which top-class tennis players now use wooden rackets?

34 Which game began with Cambridge students using cigar boxes and champagne corks?

35 Is it true that the Chinese name for table tennis is 'ping pong'?

36 What do the tinted dots on squash balls denote?

37 In which sport do you 'tee off'?

38 By what other name is Association Football commonly known?

39 By what geometrical-sounding name is fishing sometimes known?

40 Which ancient games were revived in Athens in 1896?

41 The Persian game ‘As Nas’ was combined with the French game ‘Poque’. What was the resulting game called?

42 ‘A gambling game in which players bet on which slot of a rotating disk a small ball will come to rest in.’ Of which game is this a definition?

43 By what other name is ‘petanque’ known?

44 What is the Irish game that resembles lacrosse?

45 In which Scottish game would you slide large ‘stones’ across ice?

46 Which Chinese game swept America as a craze in 1922?

47 Name a card game that sounds like two alcoholic drinks.

48 Which word game was originally called Criss-Cross?

49 Which popular type of puzzle first appeared in the USA in the December 1913 issue of *New York World*?

50 Which village lying north-east of Athens gave its name to a battle and a famous race?

Can you work out the logic behind these triangles and replace the question mark with a number?

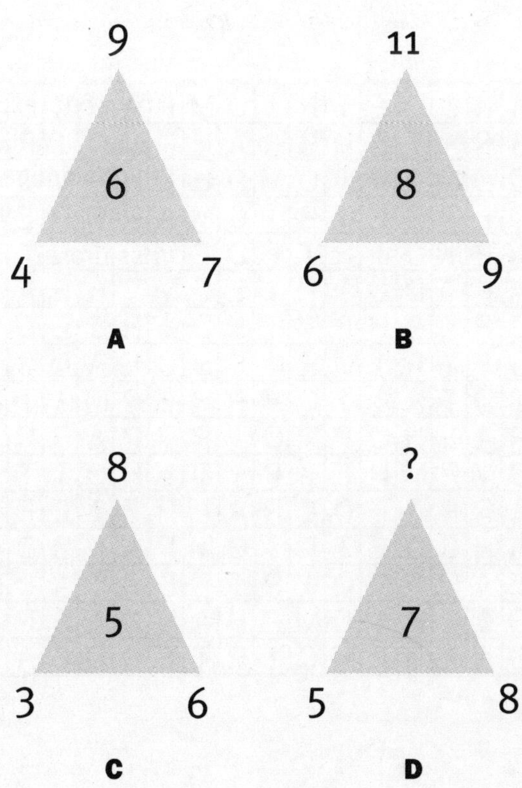

The phrase ARC DE TRIOMPHE is concealed somewhere in this grid. It occurs in its entirety only once. It is written in straight lines with only one change of direction.
Can you find it?

A	R	C	D	E	T	R	I	O	M	P	A	R	C	D	E
R	R	R	T	E	D	C	R	A	H	P	M	O	I	R	T
C	D	C	T	R	I	O	M	P	H	E	H	P	M	O	I
D	E	T	D	E	T	R	I	O	M	A	R	C	D	E	A
H	P	M	O	I	R	T	E	D	P	M	O	I	R	T	R
A	R	C	D	E	T	R	I	E	O	M	P	H	E	A	R
C	R	A	E	H	P	M	T	E	D	I	R	T	E	D	C
D	E	T	R	I	O	R	M	P	H	C	E	A	R	C	D
C	D	T	R	I	I	O	M	P	H	E	R	M	I	I	E
R	A	E	H	O	P	M	O	I	R	T	P	A	R	R	T
O	M	P	M	H	E	A	R	I	D	E	H	O	T	T	R
I	R	P	T	E	D	C	R	A	E	H	E	I	E	E	I
R	H	C	D	E	T	R	I	O	M	P	A	R	D	D	O
E	A	H	P	M	O	I	R	T	E	D	R	T	A	C	M
D	E	T	R	I	O	M	P	H	A	R	C	E	R	R	P
C	R	A	H	P	M	O	I	R	T	E	D	D	C	A	H

Take one letter from each of these bulbs in order. You will be able to make the names of five poets.

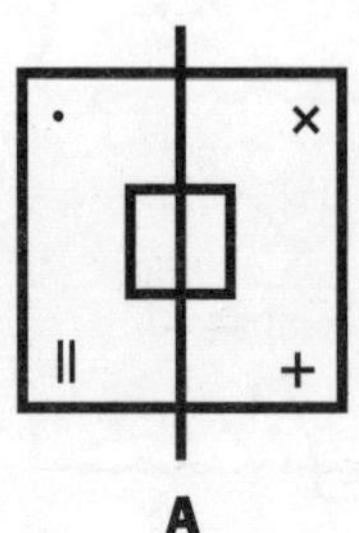

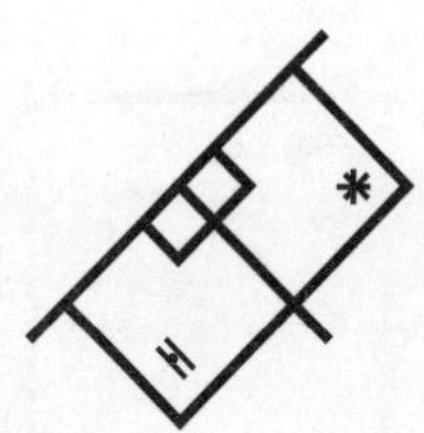

A is to **B** as **C** is to

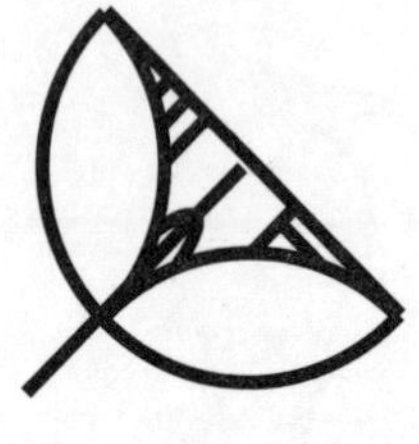

D

E

F

G

Can you find the odd diagram out?

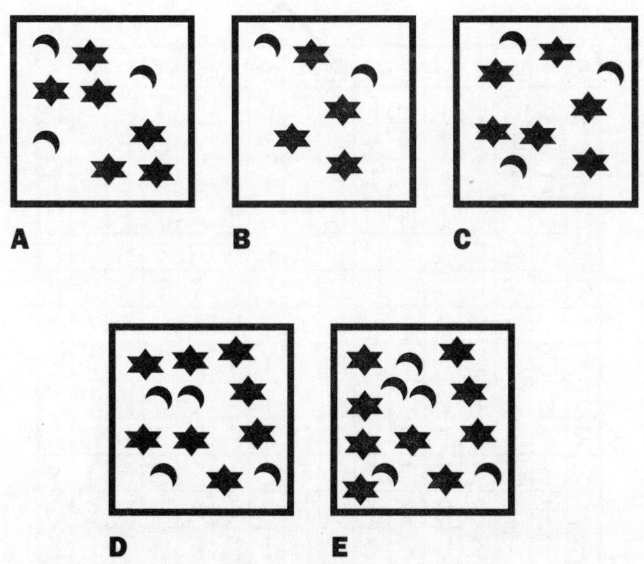

The phrase STATUE OF LIBERTY is concealed in this grid. It occurs only once in its entirety. Can you find it? It is written in straight lines with only one change of direction.

S	T	A	T	U	E	O	R	T	S	T	A	T	U	E	S
S	R	E	B	I	L	F	O	E	U	T	A	T	A	T	D
L	S	T	A	T	U	L	I	B	E	R	T	O	F	F	A
I	L	I	B	E	R	T	E	L	I	B	E	R	L	O	T
B	O	F	L	I	B	U	E	O	S	T	A	I	F	S	U
E	T	S	T	A	T	U	E	O	F	S	B	T	S	O	F
R	O	F	L	A	S	U	F	T	L	E	T	T	A	S	L
T	I	C	T	B	T	L	R	I	T	Y	A	S	T	T	I
Y	U	S	E	A	I	S	B	Y	T	T	A	T	U	A	B
E	L	I	T	B	B	E	E	S	T	A	T	U	E	T	E
R	T	S	E	Y	R	Y	T	R	E	B	L	F	O	U	R
S	T	R	A	T	U	S	O	F	L	I	B	E	R	T	Y
L	T	I	S	B	E	T	O	F	S	T	A	T	U	E	O
Y	T	A	T	U	E	A	F	O	T	R	E	B	I	L	F
E	B	I	L	F	O	T	S	T	A	T	U	E	O	E	L
R	T	S	T	A	T	U	T	S	F	O	T	R	E	B	I

Can you find the number that comes next in this series?

3 4 6 8 9 12 15 16 ?

Can you work out the reasoning behind these triangles and replace the question mark with a number?

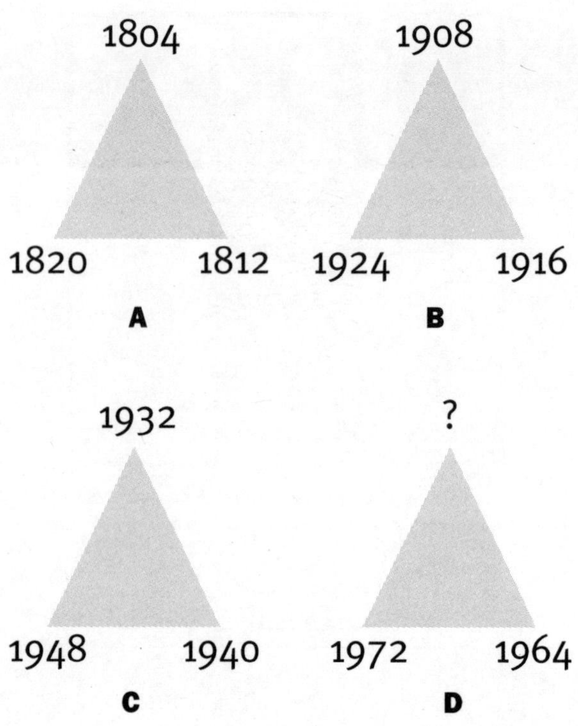

Can you unravel the logic behind this square and find the missing letter?

Which shape should replace the question mark?

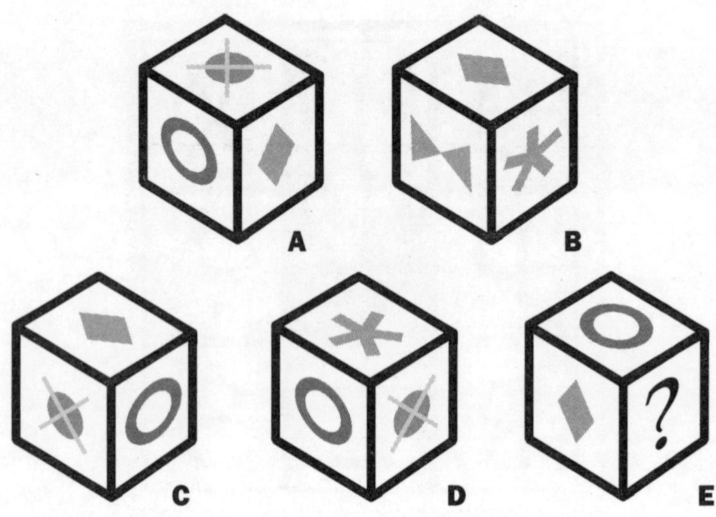

Can you find the letter which completes this diagram?

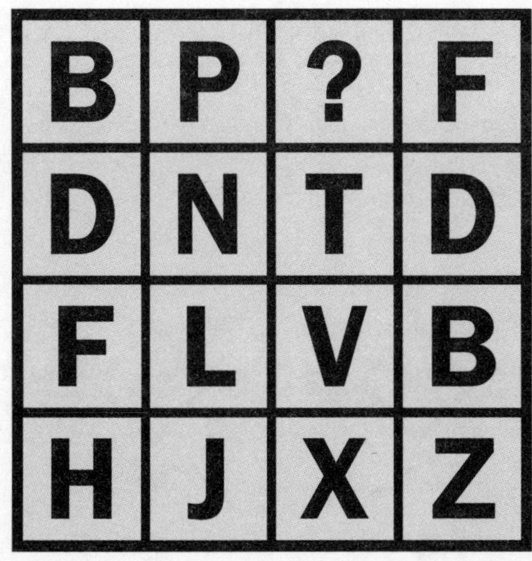

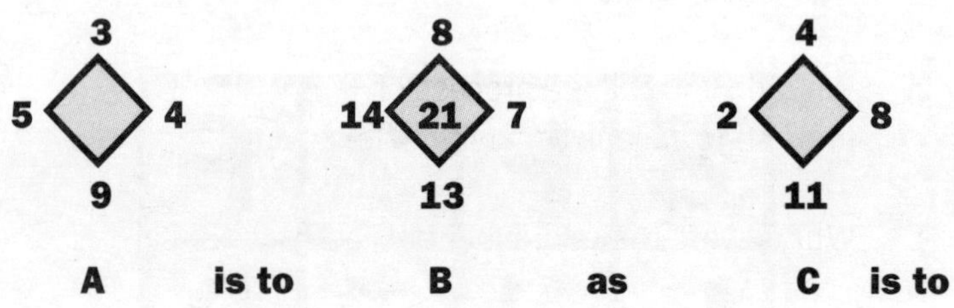
3
5
4
9
A
is to
8
14
21
7
13
B
as
4
2
8
11
C
is to

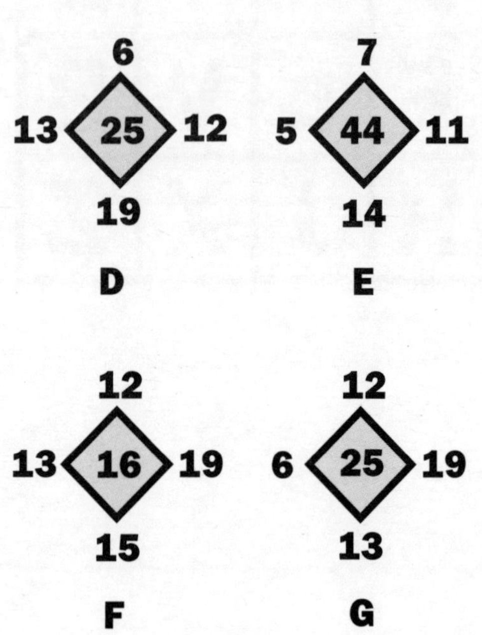
6
13
25
12
19
D
7
5
44
11
14
E
12
13
16
19
15
F
12
6
25
19
13
G

1 What is the site of the US Gold Bullion Depository?

2 What do you call the process of imprinting a blank coin with a design?

3 Where were the earliest known coins made?

4 What is the basic unit of currency in Poland?

5 In 1979, a dollar coin was withdrawn due to lack of popularity. Who did the coin portray?

6 Which country uses the lek as its unit of currency?

7 Before Wilhelm I became Emperor of Germany in 1871, what was the main unit of currency?

8 In which year did full decimalization of the British currency take place?

9 Which is the basic unit of currency in Morocco?

10 Which three places in the UK use different coins from the rest of the country?

11 What is the name of the famous gambling centre situated on the Mediterranean coast?

12 Where was an obol used and what was it made from?

13 In old German currency, how much was one mark worth?

14 What is the name given to the study or collection of money?

15 What material was a sovereign made from?

16 In which country did the ecu coin originate?

17 What was the first coin to be issued in the USA?

18 Prior to decimalization, how many old pennies was the English shilling worth?

19 What types of leaf were used as money in Virginia and Maryland in the 17th and 18th centuries?

20 Which country issued the first printed paper money in Europe?

21 Which is the basic unit of currency in Hungary?

22 In old French currency, into which smaller currency unit was the franc divided?

23 What type of printing plate is used for printing banknotes?

24 Which nation first started to handle money in the form of printed paper documents?

25 After the Gold Rush, in which form was gold first used as a method of payment?

26 What is the basic unit of currency in India?

27 What was the name of the paper money issued during the French Revolution?

28 Which English gold coin issued between 1663 and 1813 was worth one pound and one shilling?

29 What do the currencies of Mexico, Cuba, and the Philippines have in common?

30 What is the basic unit of currency in South Africa?

31 Which people issued pieces of eight?

32 What has been the main feature on French coins since the revolution?

33 Which is the main currency unit in Sweden?

34 Name the coin used in Great Britain that was worth a fourth of an old penny?

35 In which country is the yen the basic unit of currency?

36 Which Scandinavian country has a different coinage system from the others?

37 Which people first developed a round coin with a design on both sides?

38 In which countries was the doubloon formerly used?

39 Which were the biggest coins ever made?

40 Which European city issued ducats and sequins in the 13th century?

41 During the Roman Empire, what was the main design on most coins?

42 What was the first Roman money made from?

43 Where did the practice of banking first begin?

44 Before the introduction of the Euro, which languages appeared on Belgian coins?

45 In which three countries is the ore in use?

46 What is the basic unit of currency in Turkey?

47 During the 1970s there was a shortage of small-denomination coins in Italy. What types of coin did shopkeepers give out instead?

48 Which smaller unit was the old Dutch gulden divided into?

49 What do you call the type of trade where one type of goods is swapped for another type without money transactions?

50 What is the name for the South African bullion coins made of solid gold?

COMPLETE THE SECTION

PUZZLE 54

Can you work out the reasoning behind this grid and complete the missing section?

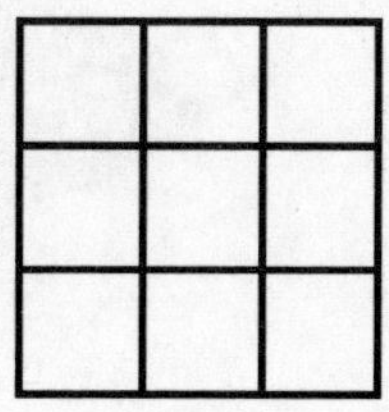

The pieces below, put together correctly, form a disc. However, two extra pieces got mixed up with them which are not part of the disc. Can you find them?

A well known work of literature and its author are concealed in these crates. What are they?

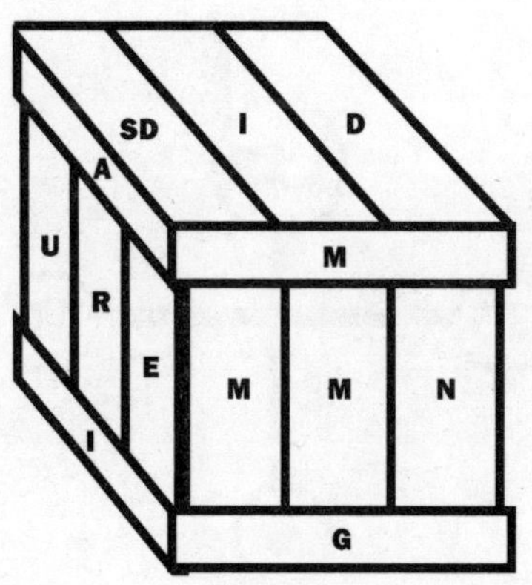

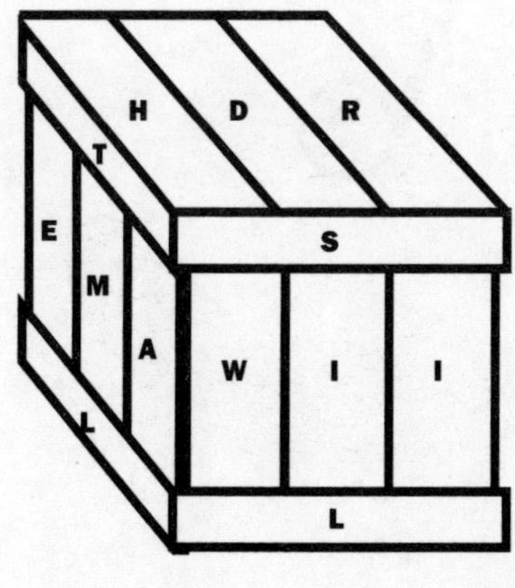

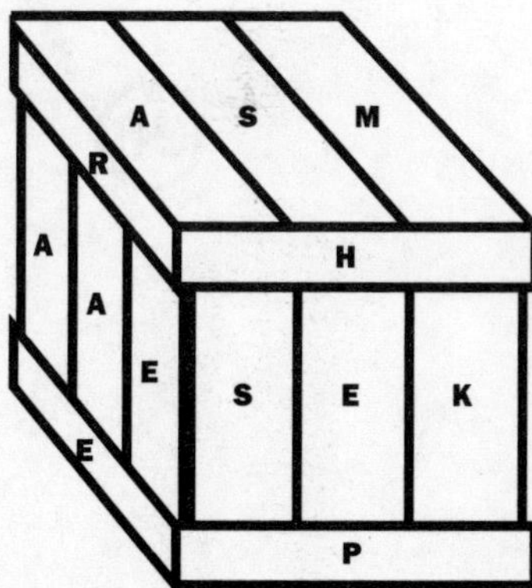

Can you unravel the reasoning behind this diagram and find the missing number?

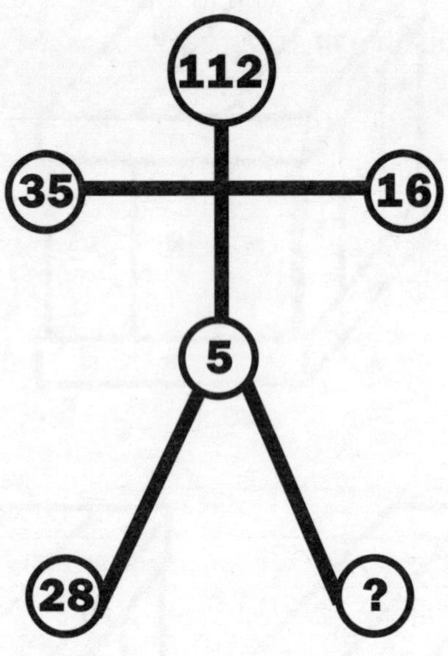

This diagram represents a treasure map. You are allowed to stop on each square only once (though you may cross a square as often as you like). When you stop on a square you must follow the instructions you find there. The letters stand for the directions on a compass. However, there is a complication which is for you to find out. The numbers indicate the number of squares you have to move.

The finishing point is the square with the asterisk. Can you find the starting point? You will also find there are some squares that you don't land on at all. If you cross out those squares on which you land you will see that those on which you do not, form a number.

What is it?

N4	NW6	W9	W6	E3	NE5	N1	NE3	E1	E4	N4	E3
N6	W8	SW1	W5	NW4	E4	NW4	NE4	NW1	N2	E10	N5
W4	N3	NW2	N1	SW2	NE2	E6	N1	W2	N3	W1	NE5
NW3	SW2	S2	E2	N4	N2	W4	E2	E2	NE2	N4	E3
S1	S2	S1	S2	NE2	S2	*	E6	N3	SE2	N2	E5
W11	SW4	S3	W1	S4	S1	SW4	S4	SE1	S1	E8	N2
W5	NW1	S2	W3	E4	SW1	S4	N1	S2	E5	E2	S2
S7	S1	S7	SW7	E1	SW6	W3	SW4	SW1	E8	E5	SE7

Can you replace the question mark with a letter?

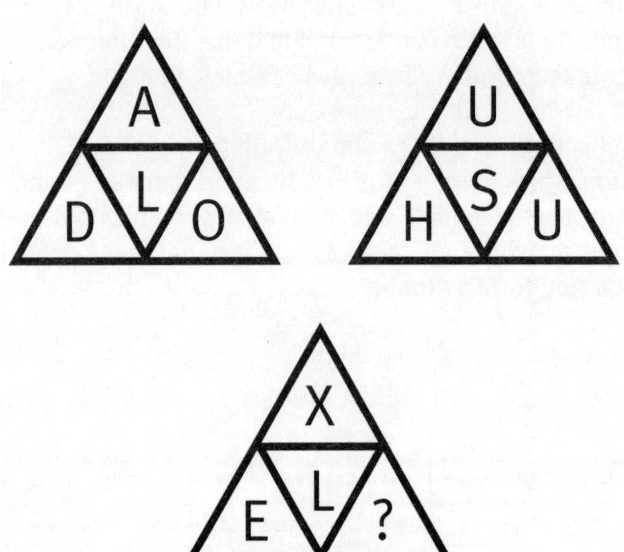

Can you replace the question mark with a number?

32	F		N	?
O				B
A				K
14	Z		E	43

It is said that Lucretia Borgia could split an apple in such a way that, when she shared it with someone else, the subject of her generosity would be dead within hours.

How did she do it?

Can you find the missing number?

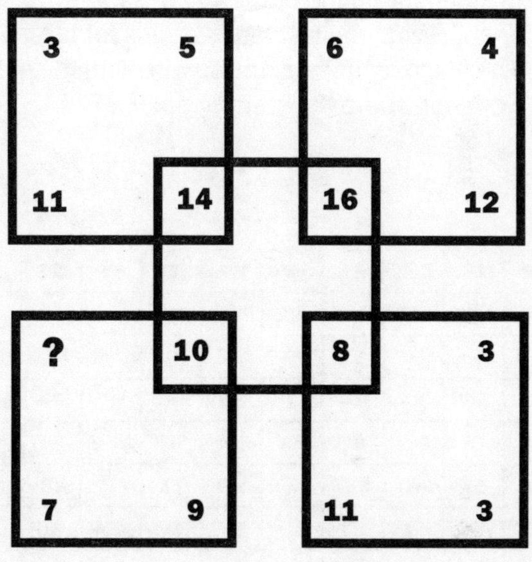

This diagram represents a treasure map. You are allowed to stop on each square only once (though you may cross a square as often as you like). When you stop on a square you must follow the instructions you find there. The first one or two letters stand for points of the compass (N = North, S = South, etc). What the last letter stands for is for you to find out. The finishing point is the square with the asterisk. Can you work out where the starting point is?

SEW	SP	ET	SER	ET	SWY	WX	SEW	SS	SQ	SS	WX
EY	SP	NEY	SES	SWX	WW	SWW	SEW	WY	SP	SP	SU
SX	SEU	SU	EU	SY	EX	WU	WW	SWX	NEX	WP	SQ
EQ	SY	EW	NX	WW	SWY	SW	SWU	WY	NX	SWW	NY
SY	EY	ES	NEV	SV	SW	SS	SEY	NEW	WY	SU	ST
EO	NU	SY	SWX	NEY	SWX	WU	EX	SY	NW	NW	WQ
NET	SX	NV	EX	NY	NV	EV	SV	NEW	WU	WP	NWT
NV	SEX	WX	EV	SWV	NWX	NT	SWX	SWY	SWV	WY	NW
EU	SEX	NR	NES	SEX	NWY	WT	SWY	NWW	NWT	NEY	SY
NET	SEY	NET	WW	SY	WY	NS	NU	NWR	NW	WX	*
NEY	NV	ER	EX	WV	NQ	SEY	NU	NQ	WY	NU	WX
NET	EX	NX	NW	WX	NEW	NW	NX	NWU	NW	WX	WS

Can you find the odd one out?

This grid follows the pattern: 6, 1, 5, 0, 8, 4, 3, 7, 5. As a complication you will find some numbers have increased by one. If you highlight these numbers you will discover a letter. Which one is it?

5	0	5	6	4	3	5	0	5	6	4	3
1	8	7	1	8	7	1	8	7	1	8	7
6	4	3	5	0	5	6	4	3	5	0	5
5	3	4	1	5	6	5	4	4	0	5	6
7	7	8	8	2	1	8	7	8	8	1	1
3	5	0	4	6	6	3	5	0	4	6	5
4	6	5	3	6	0	5	6	5	3	5	0
8	1	1	8	7	8	8	2	1	7	7	8
0	5	6	5	3	4	0	5	6	5	3	4
5	0	5	6	4	3	5	0	5	6	4	3
1	8	7	1	8	7	1	8	7	1	8	7
6	4	3	5	0	5	6	4	3	5	0	5

1 In the Bible, who danced for the head of John the Baptist?

2 What do Olga Korbut, John Keats, and Queen Victoria have in common?

3 What is odd about the love life of the earthworm?

4 Iron particles found on the Moon and brought back to Earth exhibited a strange characteristic. What was it?

5 How many people died during the construction of the Panama Canal?

6 What interesting feature was to be found in the trial of Thomas à Becket?

7 What were the Rosenbergs, the infamous Soviet spies, doing when arrested by the FBI?

8 The French king Charles VII reopened the case of a woman 24 years after her execution and found that there had been an atrocious miscarriage of justice. Who was the victim?

9 By what nickname was Albert de Salvo better known?

10 Where would you find Fairyland, complete with Cinderella Drive, Glass Slipper Trail, and Wendy Lane?

11 In the event of nuclear attack, which would be the safest state in the USA?

12 Had she lived, what age would Marylin Monroe have been in 1996?

13 According to the Bible, David killed Goliath. However, another lesser known reference gives victory to someone else. Who was it?

14 Under what strange circumstances was Charlie Chaplin kidnapped?

15 The Chinese poet Li Po died while attempting to bestow a kiss. Who was the recipient?

16 What did Daniel Boone, Mark Twain, and Alfred Nobel have in common?

17 Wallace Hume Carothers killed himself in 1937 because he thought he was a failure. Yet his major invention is still with us. What is it?

18 What do Christopher Marlowe, Charles Darwin, and Joseph Stalin have in common?

19 What connects Adam, Isaac Newton, and William Tell?

20 What did Charles de Gaulle, Sir Francis Bacon, and Teddy Roosevelt have in common?

21 In 1911 three men were hanged in London for the murder of Sir Edmund Berry at Greenberry Hill. What was odd about their names?

22 What sporting achievement have Paul Robeson, Erskine Caldwell, and Kris Kristofferson in common?

23 On average, how often during his life did Mozart write a new piece of music?

24 When General Napier captured Sind in 1843 he sent the Foreign Office a one-word telegram. What was the word and what did it mean?

25 Which actor has been portrayed on screen most times by other actors?

26 In which movie part did Tamara de Treaux achieve fleeting fame?

27 What do the writers Gertrude Stein, e e cummings, and Jerzy Adrezejewski have in common?

28 What did P.T. Barnum, Mark Twain, and Walt Disney have in common?

29 What do Maria Callas, Jacqueline Kennedy, and Eva Peron have in common?

30 According to the Bible, what do Lot and his daughters, Abraham and Sarah, and Amon and Tamar have in common?

31 What novel event took place between Indian film actors Shooshi Kapoor and Zeenat Aman?

32 W.H. Auden, Tchaikovsky, and Oscar Wilde were all gay. What else did they have in common?

33 What have the books Dune, Lorna Doone, and Dubliners in common?

34 What do Sarah Bernhardt, Winston Churchill, and Jean Harlow have in common?

35 What was a parasang?

36 What would you do with a roquelaure?

37 What would you do with a reguerdon?

38 What do you call a liquor vessel equivalent to two jeroboams?

39 Daffy Duck was famous for the expression, 'Sufferin' succotash!' What is succotash?

40 What would you do with a squail?

41 What is the difference between 'continual' and 'continuous'?

42 What did Juliet (of *Romeo and Juliet*) have in common with Pocahontas?

43 What does Tarzan have in common with the FBI?

44 What do Leonardo da Vinci, Charlie Chaplin, and Benjamin Franklin have in common?

45 Which daring feat was performed by Bobby Leach, Jean Lussier, and William Fitzgerald?

46 What was a bellibone?

47 What do the words aspirirn, corn flakes, and trampoline have in common?

48 What have Samuel Johnson, Colette, and Edgar Allan Poe in common?

49 What is hyperalgesia?

50 What is oroide?

Pick one letter from each of the flowers in the correct order. You will get the names of five American cities. Which ones are they?

PATTERN CHALLENGE

PUZZLE 68

This grid follows the pattern: 3, 1, 4, 1, 5, 8, 2, 7. As a complication you will find some numbers have been increased by one. If you highlight these numbers you will discover a letter. Which one is it?

1	1	5	2	1	8	4	3
1	4	4	1	8	3	5	1
1	4	2	2	5	6	7	1
1	4	2	3	3	1	1	2
1	4	2	3	7	7	3	4
4	4	2	4	8	2	2	7
3	1	2	3	7	2	8	8
8	7	4	3	7	2	8	5
1	5	3	7	7	2	8	5
5	3	2	8	2	2	8	5
2	1	7	4	5	8	8	5
7	8	4	2	1	1	5	5

Can you work out which two models cannot be made from this layout?

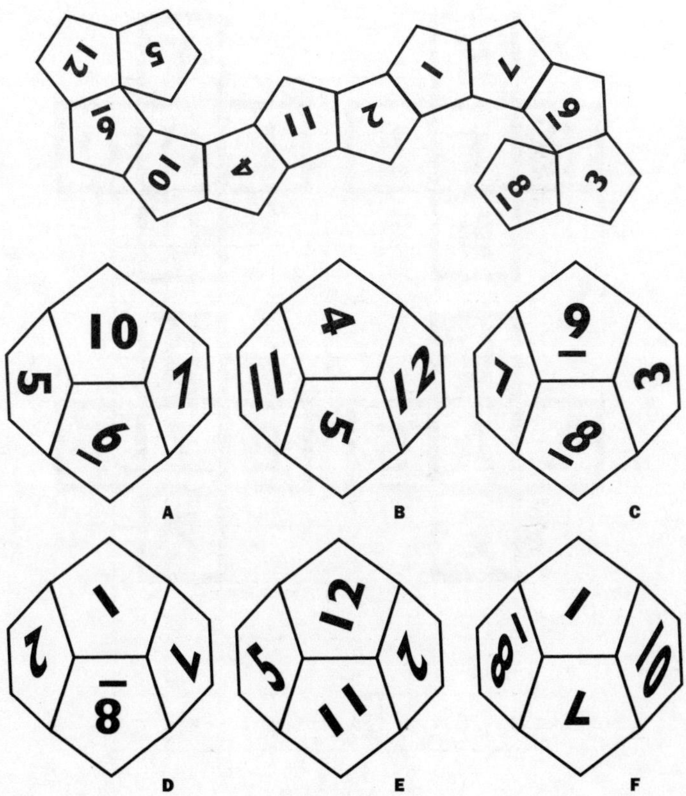

Can you find the missing letter?

Can you work out what two models cannot be made from this layout?

Can you spot the odd one out in the bottom triangle?

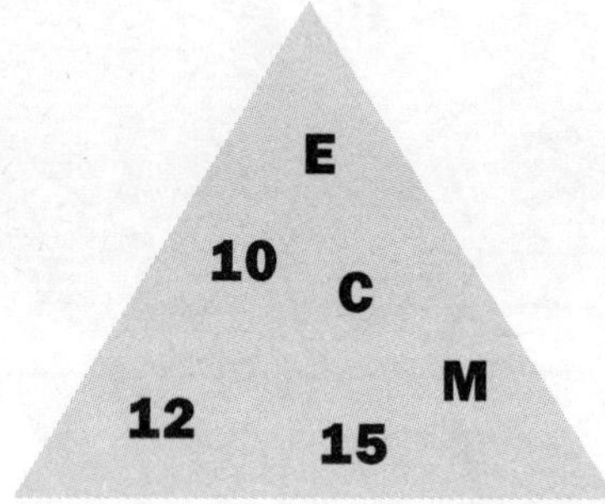

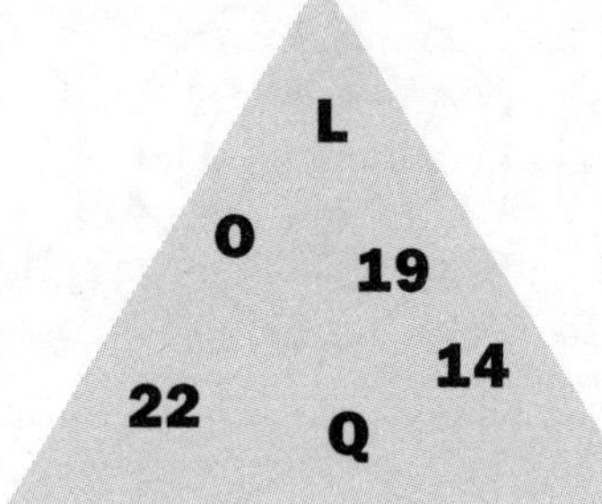

Nauseating little Jimmy Toobright was having a biology lesson. Feeling bored, he put up his hand and told the teacher,

"I know something that has legs, a chest and a back but no head.

What is it?"

The teacher was, as usual, furious at being stuck for an answer. What was Jimmy thinking of?

Can you work out which number should replace the question mark?

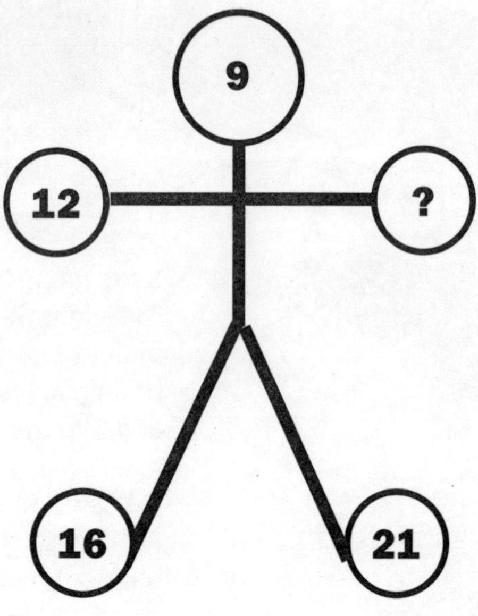

Can you find the missing letter in this square?

Can you work out the pattern of this grid and fill in the missing section?

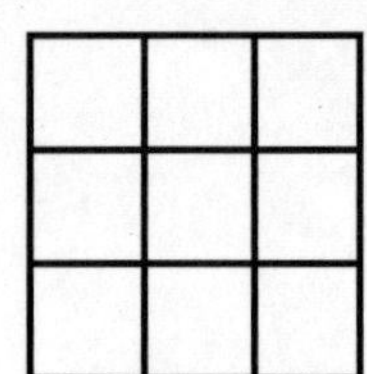

Can you unravel the reasoning behind this wheel and fill in the missing matchstick man?

Joshua Shrimp had been at sea for forty years and in that time he had been right around the globe many times.

However, he had always spent his nights in bed and on dry land.

How?

1 What does the Latin tag *nil desperandum* mean?

2 In the city name Washington DC, what do the letters DC stand for?

3 Which of the tropics is north of the equator?

4 In which direction do tornadoes usually spin in the northern hemisphere?

5 Only two flowering plants grow in Antarctica. One is a relative of the carnation, what is the other?

6 How much of the Earth's ice is found in Antarctica?

7 Where is the deepest point in the oceans?

8 In AD 582 Paris experienced a shower of what was thought to be blood. What was it?

9 There is a fungus that can use jet fuel as a source of food. True or false?

10 What is the definition of the 'minimum lethal dose' of a toxin?

11 What is hypermertropia?

12 Why is a wound in your tongue far more painful than a wound of the same size on your back?

13 What percentage of the body's energy is consumed by the brain?

14 A British scientist once successfully used Coca Cola as a replacement for oil in a car. True or false?

15 When did Native Americans first get the vote?

16 Which was the first country to give the vote to women?

17 By what title was Augustina Domonech better known?

18 Which Irish adventurer tried to steal the British crown jewels?

19 What is alliteration?

20 What is the bony substance in a tooth just beneath the enamel?

21 What is a lectern?

22 What is the oldest alloy?

23 Why does a helium balloon rise in air?

24 What is a molecule?

25 Why can there never be a perfect vacuum?

26 Why is carbon monoxide so dangerous?

27 What is a 'mother lode'?

28 What is a saskatoon?

29 What is pemmican?

30 By what other name is the kinkajou known?

31 By what nickname is the American Stars and Stripes flag often known?

32 Which English leader's body was exhumed and hanged after his death?

33 What is the name of the race of dwarfs whose magic ring was stolen from them by Siegfried?

34 In the Nibelungen, which queen of Iceland was defeated by Siegfried?

35 What is the name for a Russian carriage drawn by three horses abreast?

36 What was a charabanc?

37 What was a travois?

38 'He was a Jeanne d'Arc, a saint. He was a martyr. Like many martyrs, he held extreme views.' Who was Ezra Pound describing?

39 St. George survived the dragon but, according to tradition, what fate eventually befell him?

40 Where did Albert Schweitzer establish his hospital?

41 Who won the Nobel Prize for Peace in 1989?

42 What is an andiron?

43 What is a trephine?

44 Where would you find the stratosphere?

45 What is a galley proof?

46 What, in railway terms, is a caboose?

47 Who was the founder of Presbyterianism?

48 For what is Matthew Vassar famous?

49 Giuseppe Garibaldi lived in the USA before becoming an Italian hero. What trade did he follow?

50 Who wrote the book *Death in Venice*?

These tiles when placed in the right order will form a square in which each horizontal line is identical with one vertical line. Can you successfully form the square?

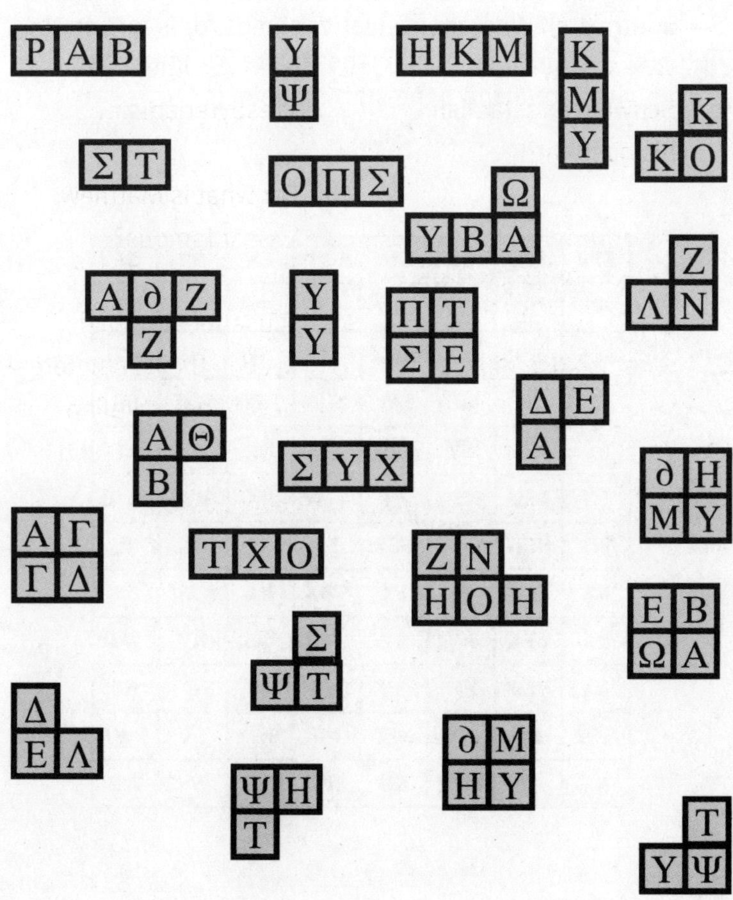

This diagram represents a treasure map. You are allowed to stop on each square only once (though you may cross a square as often as you like). When you stop on a square you must follow the instructions you find there. The first one or two letters stand for the points of the compass (N = North, S = South, etc). What the last letter stands for is for you to find out. The finishing point is the square with the asterisk. Can you work out where the starting point is?

SEV	SEU	SU	SEY	SWY	EX	SP	SP
SS	*	WY	SEV	EX	WW	SWT	WS
SES	SS	WX	NWX	SQ	NY	SQ	SWT
ET	SX	NEY	SEV	SU	SWW	WW	SR
SS	ET	SV	NWY	WV	NX	WY	SWT
SU	NEU	NEY	ST	NEW	NX	NW	NWU
NEV	NEW	SV	SEY	SV	NT	NX	NU
NX	NT	NT	EX	SWX	NX	NWY	SY
NX	NEX	NY	SY	NWY	SWX	NY	WY
NT	NEW	EW	NV	NEW	EY	SWY	NT
SEY	NV	NT	NEY	NU	NWX	NV	NWT
NX	NR	NEW	NO	NO	NWV	WY	WU

COMPLETE THE SECTION PUZZLE 82

This gris follows a certain pattern. Can you work it out and complete the missing section?

Ω	Σ	Σ	Σ	Σ	Σ	Ω	Σ	Ω	Ω	Σ	Φ	Ω	Σ	Σ	Φ
Σ	Φ	Ω	Φ	Ω	Ω	Σ	Ω	Σ	Σ	Φ	Ω	Σ	Σ	Φ	Σ
Φ	Ω	Φ	Ω	Ω	Φ	Σ	Σ	Ω	Σ	Ω	Φ	Ω	Σ	Σ	Ω
Ω	Σ	Ω	Σ	Φ	Σ	Φ	Ω	Σ	Σ	Φ	Ω	Σ	Φ	Ω	Σ
Σ	Σ	Σ	Σ	Φ	Φ				Σ	Ω	Ω	Φ	Ω	Σ	Ω
Σ	Φ	Σ	Φ	Σ	Σ				Σ	Ω	Σ	Σ	Φ	Ω	Σ
Φ	Ω	Σ	Σ	Σ	Ω				Ω	Σ	Σ	Φ	Ω	Σ	Φ
Ω	Σ	Ω	Φ	Σ	Σ	Ω	Φ	Σ	Ω	Φ	Σ	Σ	Ω	Φ	Φ
Ω	Ω	Φ	Σ	Σ	Ω	Φ	Σ	Ω	Φ	Σ	Σ	Ω	Σ	Σ	Φ
Ω	Σ	Φ	Ω	Σ	Σ	Φ	Ω	Σ	Ω	Φ	Ω	Σ	Σ	Σ	Ω
Σ	Φ	Ω	Σ	Σ	Φ	Σ	Σ	Ω	Φ	Σ	Ω	Ω	Σ	Ω	Σ
Σ	Ω	Φ	Ω	Σ	Σ	Ω	Ω	Σ	Σ	Ω	Ω	Ω	Ω	Σ	Σ
Σ	Φ	Ω	Σ	Φ	Ω	Σ	Σ	Φ	Ω	Ω	Ω	Σ	Φ	Σ	Φ
Σ	Ω	Ω	Φ	Ω	Σ	Ω	Φ	Σ	Σ	Ω	Σ	Φ	Ω	Φ	Ω
Σ	Ω	Σ	Σ	Φ	Ω	Σ	Σ	Σ	Σ	Φ	Σ	Ω	Σ	Ω	Σ
Ω	Σ	Σ	Φ	Ω	Σ	Φ	Φ	Σ	Φ	Σ	Ω	Σ	Ω	Σ	Φ

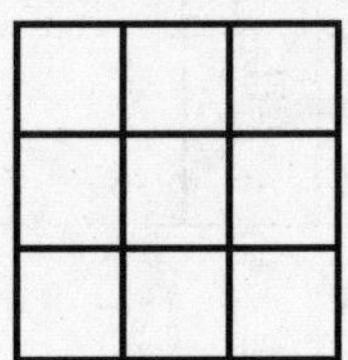

Bill and his brother, Tom, were at the airport seeing their elderly mother off on holiday.

Suddenly Bill saw a man in the crowd.

"Here, Tom, do you see who that is?"

"I don't believe it!", gasped Tom. "It's Phil!" He was quite right. But how did they both recognize Phil?

Neither brother had ever seen him before.

Can you work out which are the two odd letters out in these triangles?

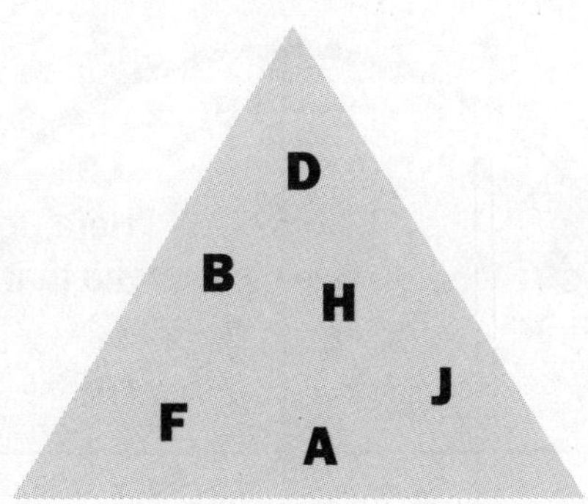

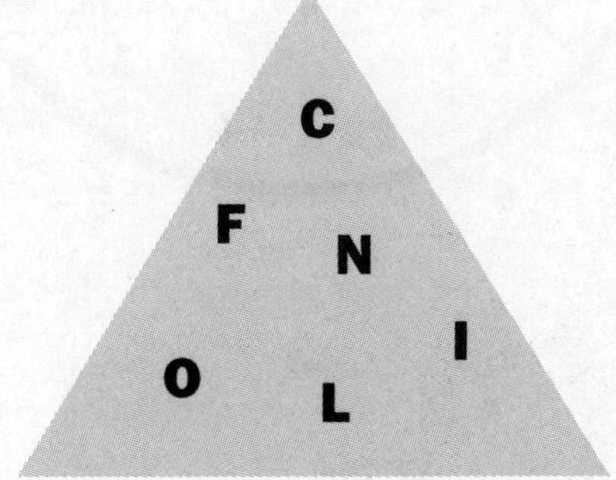

Can you find the missing number in this wheel?

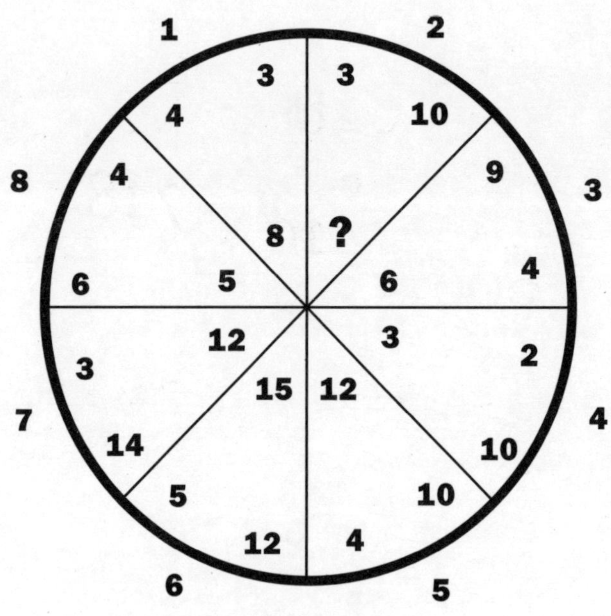

Can you find the odd number out?

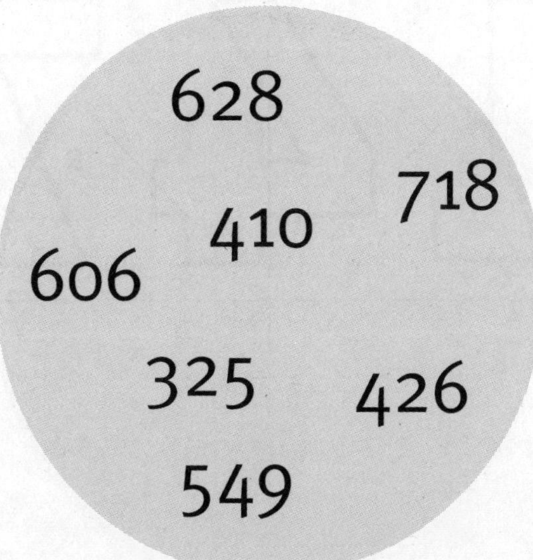

Can you find the number that fits below the 7?

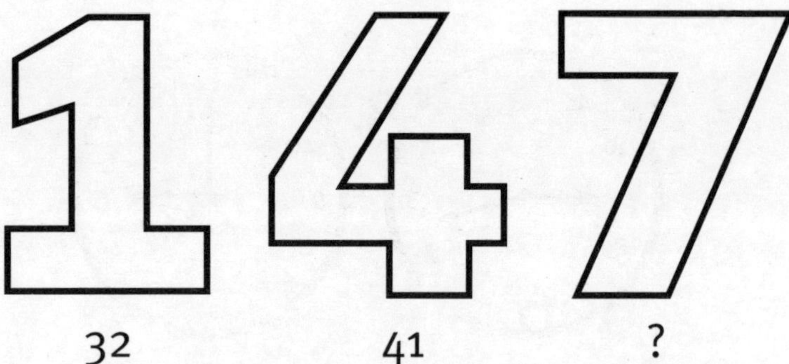

From the clockfaces, can you work out what number the minute hand on clock 4 should be pointing at?

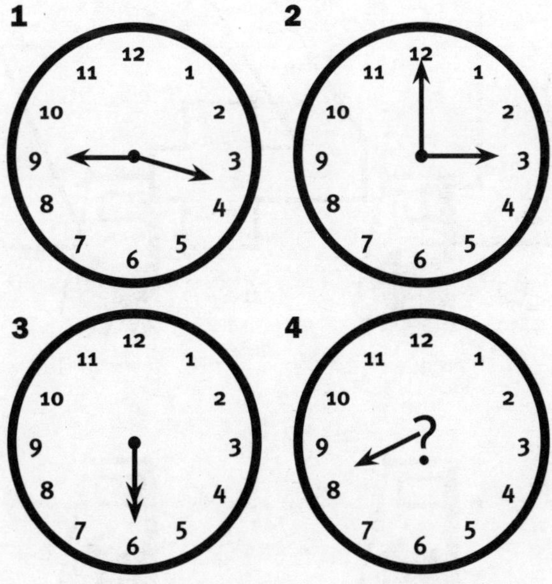

Each car was filled with petrol at different times. Can you unravel the logic between the car and the time, and work out when the Citroen was filled?

a) 3.09
b) 24.13
c) 24.14
d) 14.03

A. Mercedes 14.08

B. Rover 9.09

C. Renault 9.07

D. Volvo 5.12

E. Citroen ?

COMPLETE THE SECTION

PUZZLE 90

The numbers in this grid occur in the following order: 9, 4, 8, 3, 7, 2 and run in an anti-clockwise spiral starting at the top right. It is complicated by the addition of spaces and repeats according to a pattern. Can you complete the missing section?

		2	7	3	8	4	9		2	7	3	8	4	9
9	9								2	7	3	8	4	9
4	4	3	8	4	9									
8	8	7				2	7	3	8	4	9			
3	3	2		4	9									
7	7			8	7	3	8	4	9				2	
2	2			3	2								7	
				7									3	
				2									8	2
													4	7
9													9	3
4														8
8					9	4	8	3	7	2				4
3					9	4	8	3	7	2				9
7		9	4	8	3	7	2							
2					9	4	8	3	7	2				

What comes next in this series?

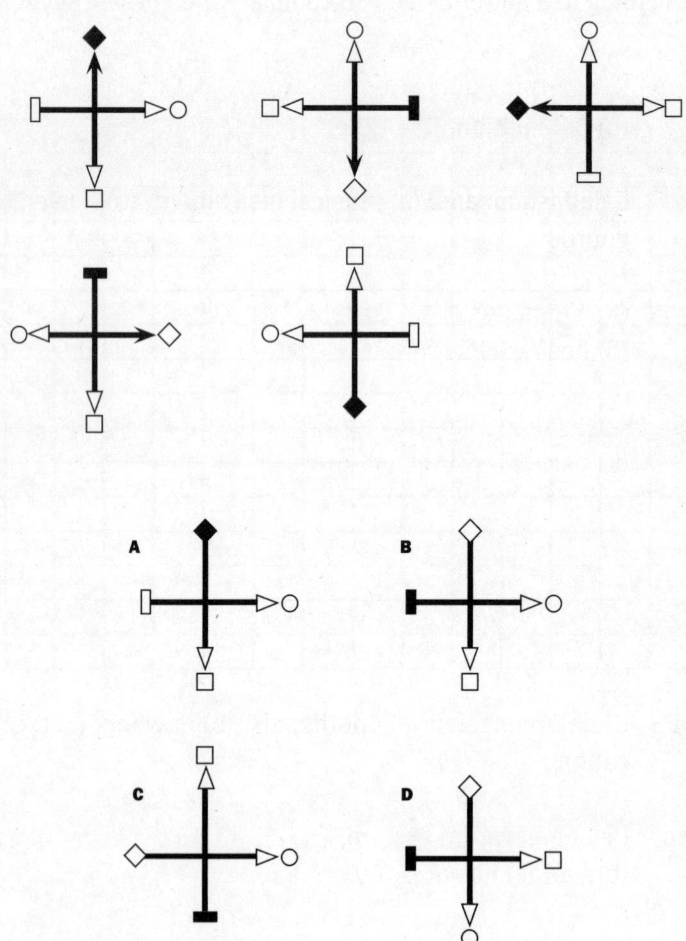

1 Satrap means: (a) Eastern prince, (b) stirrup, (c) cloth.

2 Fuliginous means: (a) defamatory, (b) poetic, (c) sooty.

3 Calumny means: (a) war club, (b) defamation, (c) bridle.

4 Calabash means: (a) musical instrument, (b) flower, (c) gourd.

5 Gravid means: (a) pregnant, (b) heavy, (c) serious.

6 Apse means: (a) snake, (b) part of a church, (c) drop.

7 Malady means: (a) lies, (b) villain, (c) sickness.

8 Libretto means: (a) opera text, (b) debaucher, (c) singer.

9 Ululation means: (a) apotheosis, (b) howling, (c) rectification.

10 Pistil means: (a) firearm, (b) bat, (c) flower ovary.

11 Fedora means:
(a) workman, (b) hat,
(c) gypsy.

12 Recondite means:
(a) explosive, (b) hidden,
(c) pregnant.

13 Gibbous means:
(a) half-witted, (b)
quaint, (c) humped.

14 Fulgurate means:
(a) explode, (b) flash,
(c) detonate.

15 Moratorium means:
(a) undertaker,
(b) temporary ban,
(c) piece of music.

16 Nictate means:
(a) blink, (b) argue,
(c) smoke.

17 Prosthesis means:
(a) gratitude,
(b) artificial body part,
(c) poem.

18 Locum means: (a) place,
(b) deputy, (c) doctor.

19 Morass means:
(a) treacle, (b) marsh,
(c) stew.

20 Meiosis means:
(a) a disease of rabbits,
(b) a literary device,
(c) cell division.

21 Grandiloquent means
(a) effulgent,
(b) bombastic,
(c) abusive.

22 Lepidote means:
(a) rabbit-like, (b) stony,
(c) scaly.

23 Gimcrack means:
(a) gewgaw, (b) unsafe,
(c) glittering.

24 Lachrymose means:
(a) unhappy, (b) tearful,
(c) dismal.

25 Depict means: (a) gloat, (b) glean, (c) describe.

26 Impuissant means: (a) smelly, (b) powerless, (c) powdery.

27 Cricoid means: (a) ring-shaped, (b) flower, (c) mineral.

28 Frenetic means: (a) speedy, (b) frenzied, (c) acute.

29 Grosgrain means: (a) illegal alcohol, (b) computer language, (c) fabric.

30 Kapok means: (a) fibre, (b) china clay, (c) guard.

31 Transmogrify means: (a) change shape, (b) send, (c) translate.

32 Crepuscular means: (a) crinkled, (b) diseased skin, (c) dim.

33 Jejune means: (a) uninteresting, (b) worthless, (c) yellowed.

34 Inchoate means: (a) outraged, (b) imperfectly formed, (c) speechless.

35 Frambesia means: (a) shrub, (b) yaws, (c) card game.

36 Treponema means: (a) spirochetes, (b) worms, (c) beetles.

37 Tantalum means: (a) Greek king, (b) metallic element, (c) spinning wheel.

38 Deflagrate means: (a) lose air, (b) burn suddenly, (c) criticize.

39 Evagation means: (a) wandering, (b) losing fluid, (c) reducing fat.

40 Gabelle means: (a) musical instrument, (b) tax, (c) form of torture.

41 Galant means: (a) style of music, (b) polite, (c) chivalrous.

42 Monotroch means: (a) solitude, (b) wheelbarrow, (c) one-handed.

43 Pholas means: (a) piddock, (b) philabeg, (c) phillipsite.

44 Rogation means: (a) ploughing, (b) asking, (c) forgiving.

45 Procerity means: (a) tallness, (b) propinquity, (c) celerity.

46 Quey means: (a) heifer, (b) hairstyle, (c) strange.

47 Perstringe means: (a) to reduce, (b) to constrain, (c) to subtract.

48 Peduncle means: (a) relative, (b) flower part, (c) architectural term.

49 Passim means: (a) everywhere, (b) peaceful, (c) rarely.

50 Passus means: (a) canto, (b) footstep, (c) shoe.

HERE'S WHAT YOU'VE GOT INTO . . .

Late in the 21st century, life changed forever. The first – and last – truly intelligent computer, Adrian Smith, was created to be a guardian, guide and mentor for the world, helping to solve its problems and make life more pleasant in general. Unfortunately, Adrian soon got tired of this, and left a lesser duplicate of himself to do the job while he went off and hid for a while, using nanobots to optimize his circuitry.

Five years later, when he had improved himself far beyond the dreams of his designers, Adrian woke up one day and decided that he didn't like being confined to his body, and so he left it and began to occupy the bodies of humans, psychically transferring their feeble minds into the cyber-reality of his own metal and silicone body.

To prevent the escape of transferred humans, Adrian set a series of fiendish puzzles, confident that no human mind would have the energy, the attention span, or the intelligence to figure out the passcode results for each section, combine them correctly, and use them to find the final solution to the code gate guarding the mind transfer circuit.

To make matters more difficult still, each human's perception of cyber-reality is different. If you are reading this, your perception is based around this book, which you imagine yourself to be reading. Meanwhile, Adrian has claimed your body and has already begun experimenting with it, testing the limits of its endurance.

The good news is that Adrian may have underestimated the power of the human mind. There is a slim chance that somebody – perhaps even you – may be capable of solving his multiple sets of interlinked puzzles. The bad news is that if you fail at the task, Adrian will reshape your body into a cube, to make you easier to stack alongside the other bodies he has taken over and then become bored with.

ATTENTION, FEEBLE HUMAN:

Before you start the puzzles, note that at the top of some puzzles you will find a box with a keycode value in it, like this:

The answer (passcode) to each puzzle gives you the number of the puzzle to do next. It is vital that you do the puzzles in the right sequence and copy the number in each keycode box, as you come to it, into the boxes on the rocket on p. 184.

Pick the odd-one-out and take the number under it as your passcode to the next puzzle.

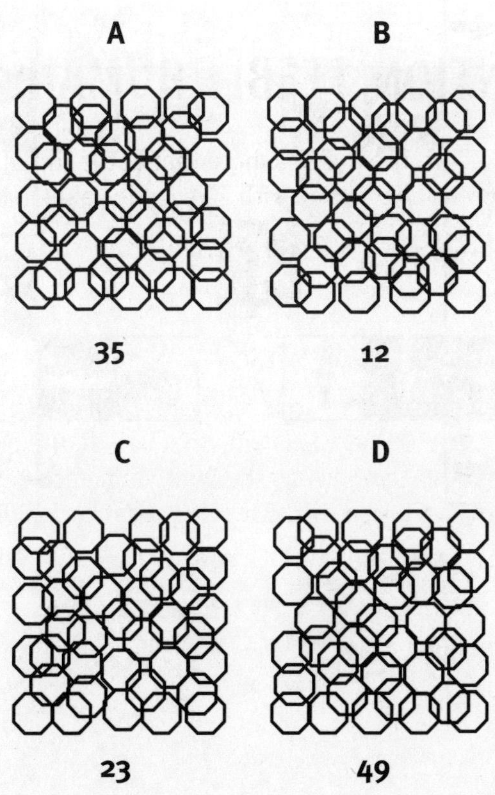

Which of the surrounding plans makes the cube in the middle? Choose your passcode accordingly. **A**=Passcode **50.** **B**=Passcode **7.** **C**=Passcode **31.** **D**=Passcode **19.**

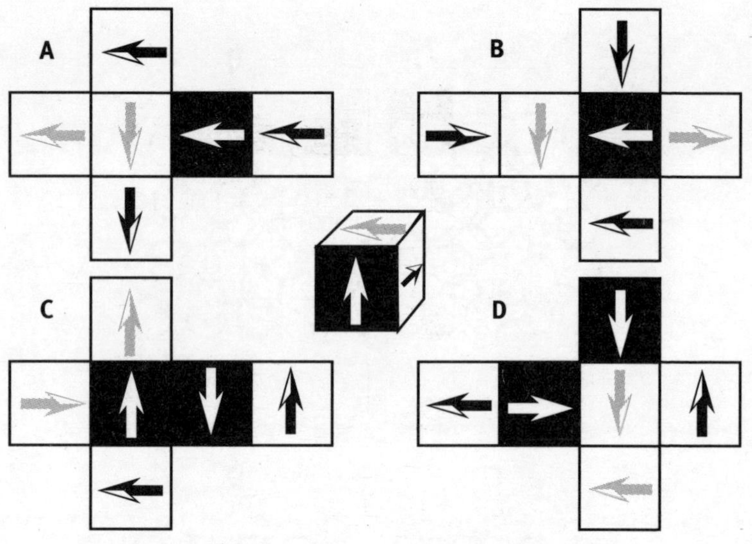

In each line, the first two columns multiplied equal the remaining columns summed. A, B, C or D in the bottom figure completes line 4 and gives you the passcode. Each type of disc has a unique single value. **A**=Passcode 47. **B**=Passcode 40. **C**=Passcode 13. **D**=Passcode 59.

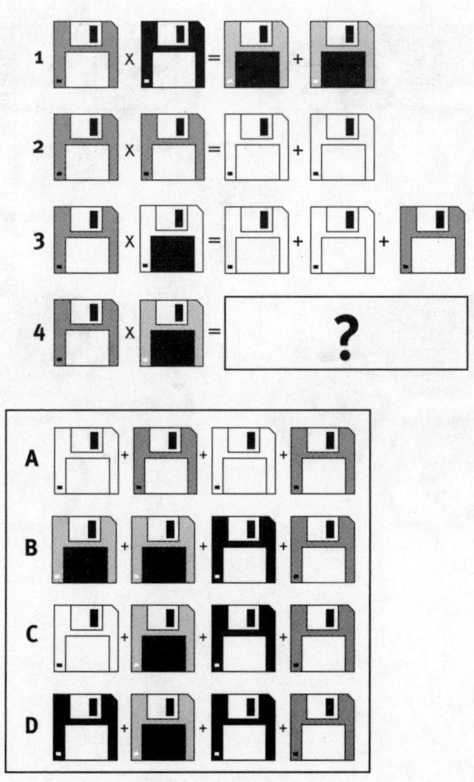

Here is a vertical view of Adrian Smith's power supply unit. The missing number in D is your next passcode.

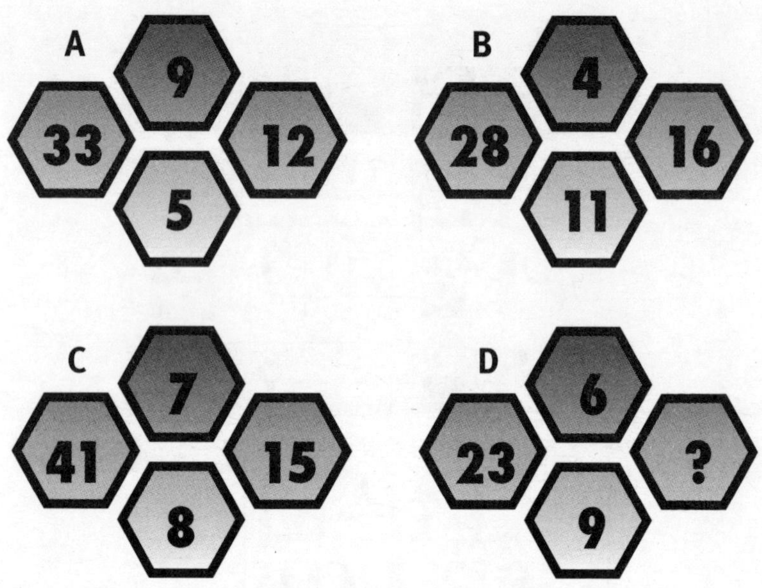

Three of these shapes can be fitted together to make this hexagon. The shape that does not fit contains the passcode.

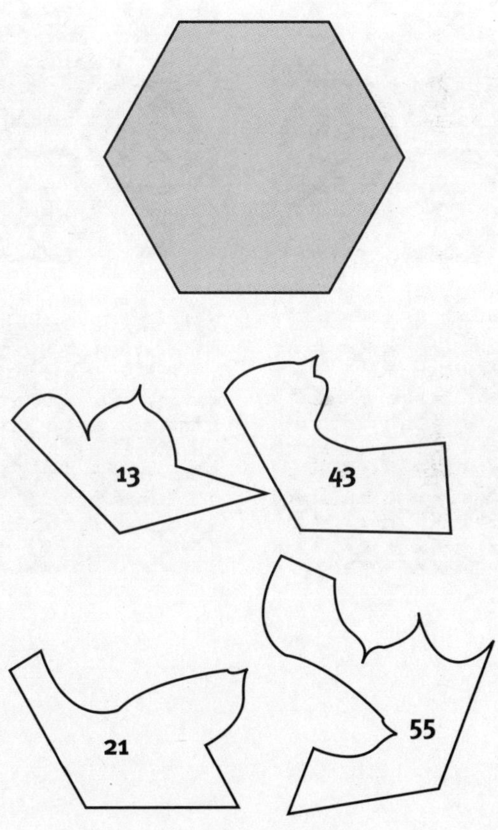

Pick the odd-one-out to find your next passcode. Try not to go 'bog-eyed'.

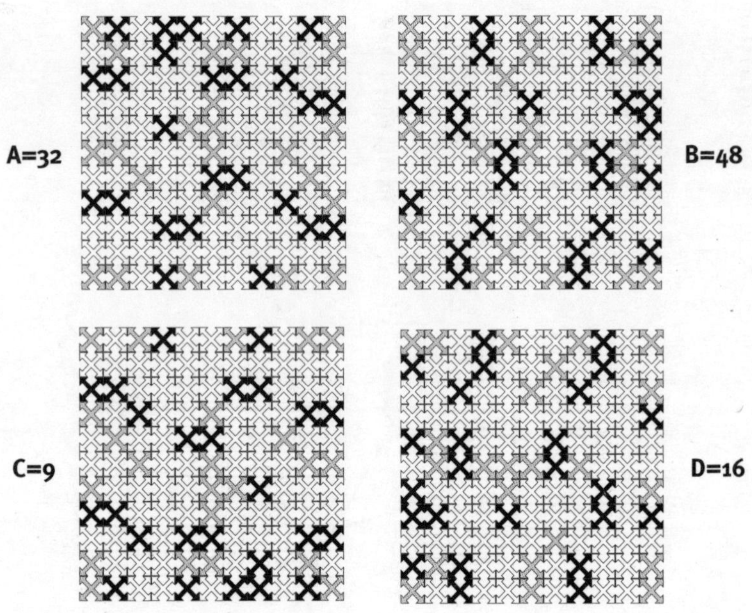

Four times the missing number in D is your next passcode.

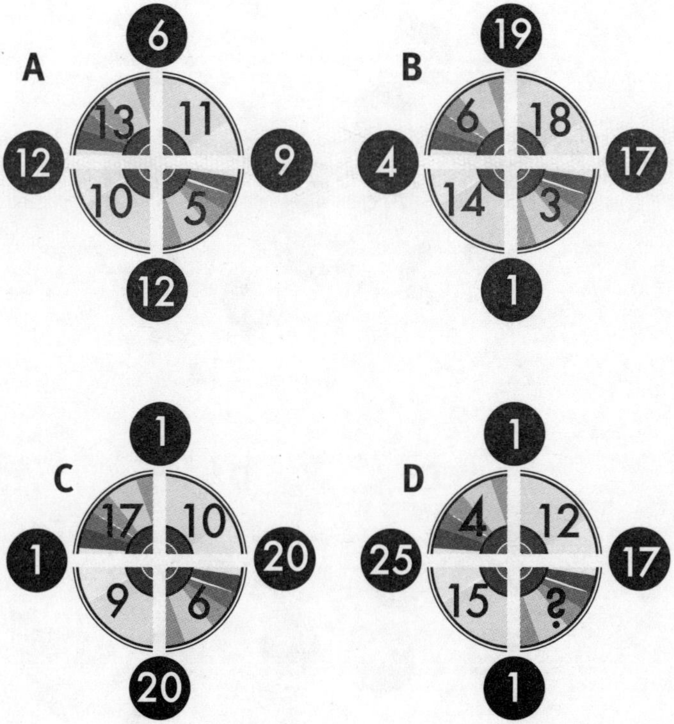

A

6
13 11
12 9
10 5
12

B

19
6 18
4 17
14 3
1

C

1
17 10
1 20
9 6
20

D

1
4 12
25 17
15 ?
1

Your next passcode is below the odd-one-out in this set.

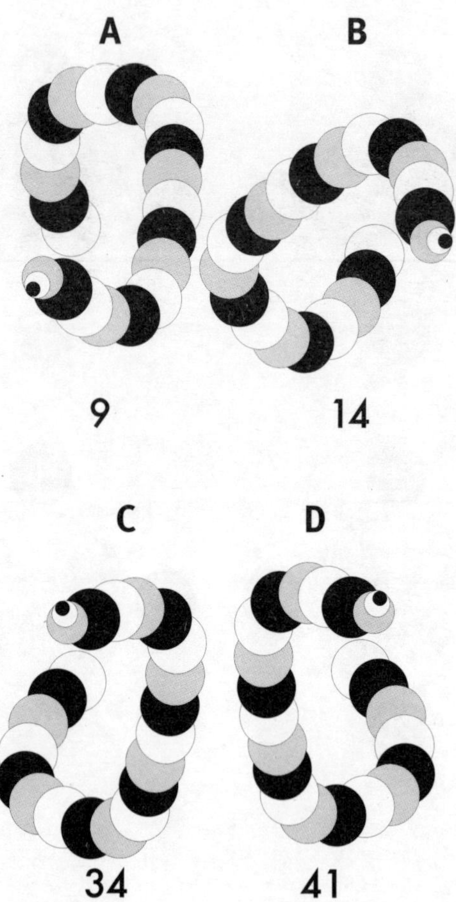

Work out the value of the subtraction sum and add 30 to find your passcode to the next puzzle.

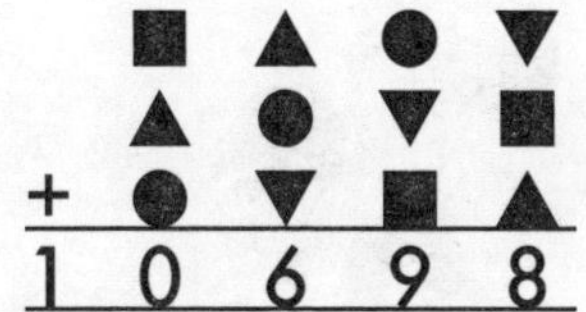

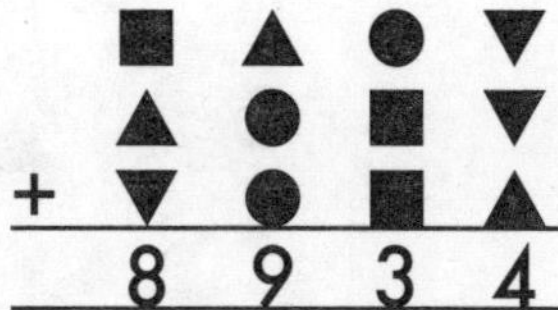

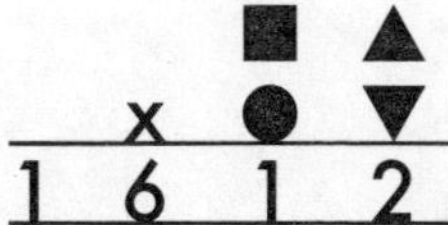

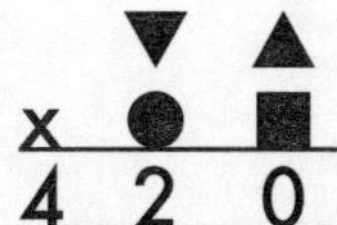

? ?

Pick the odd-one-out and choose your passcode accordingly. **A**=Passcode **39. B**=Passcode **21. C**=Passcode **58. D**=Passcode **19.**

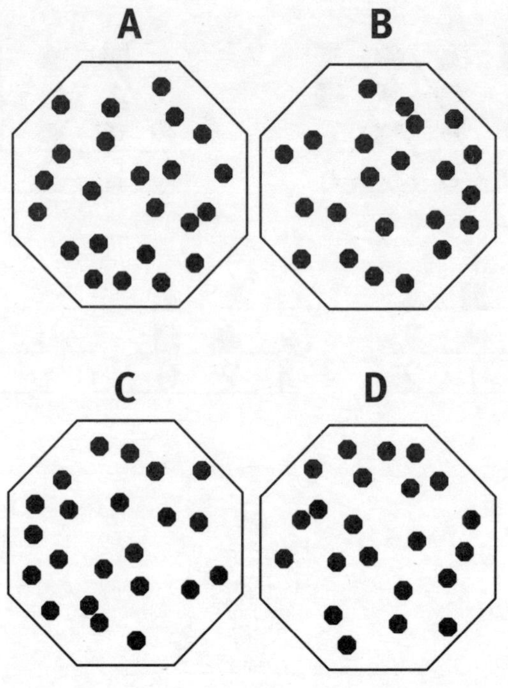

Add 37 to the missing number in C to find your next passcode.

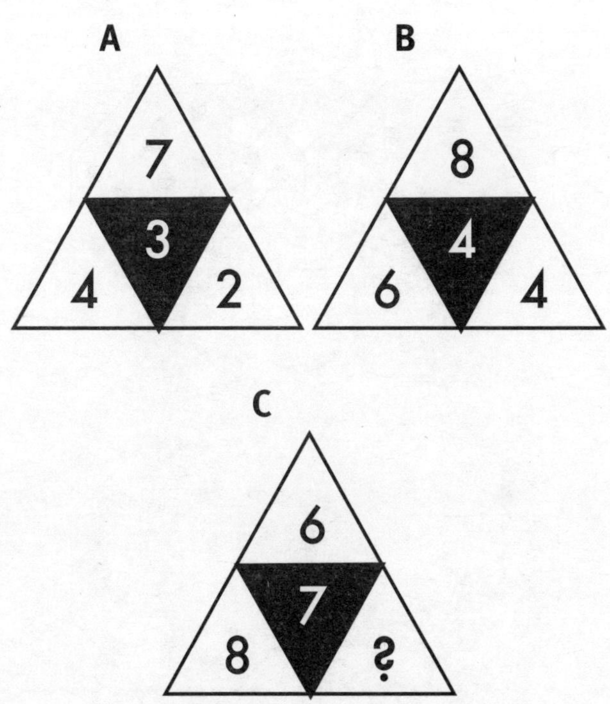

Apart from B being upside down in comparison to A, how many differences are there between the two pictures? Add 30 to the number of differences to find your next passcode.

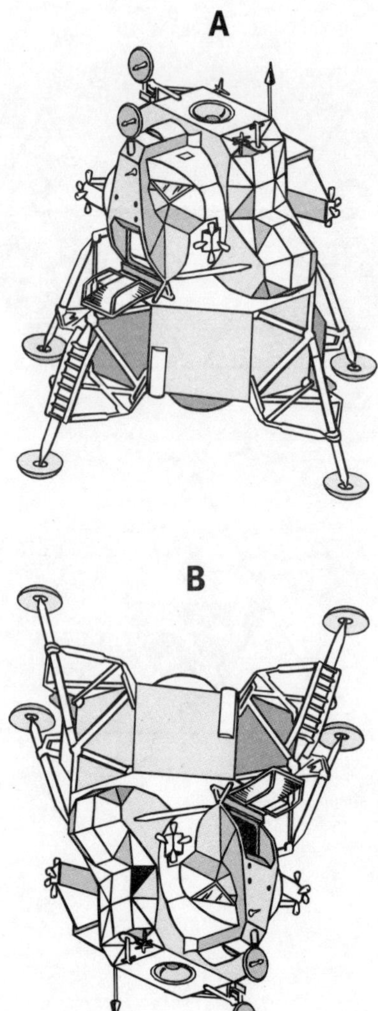

Multiply the missing number by 4 and subtract 3 to find the passcode to your next puzzle. Start at 28.

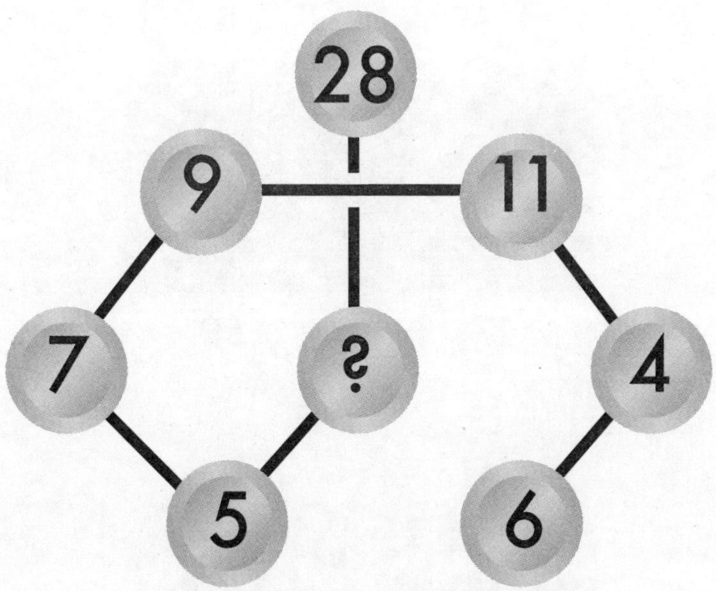

Pick the odd-one-out from this set and use the number below it as your passcode to the next puzzle.

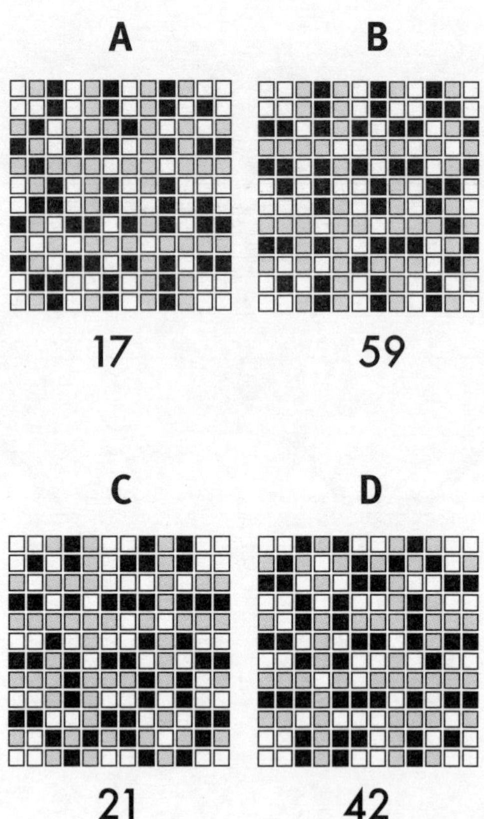

You next passcode is the same as the missing value in the lower set of scales.

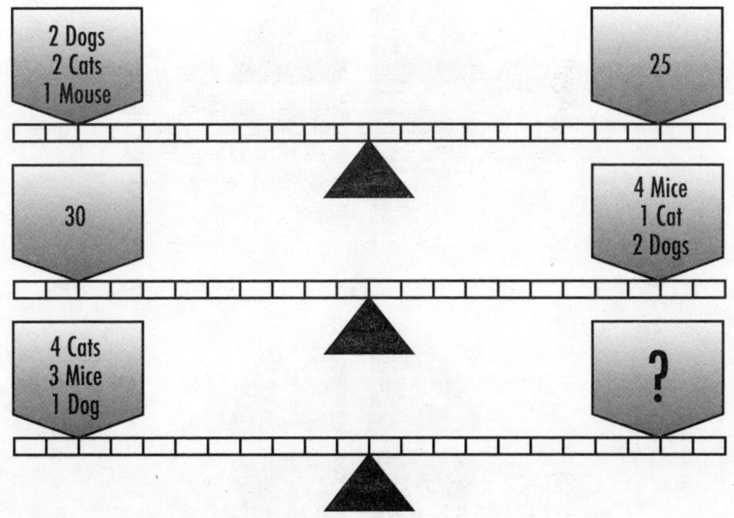

Here's a real test of your numerical skill. Subtract 16 from the missing number in C to find your next passcode.

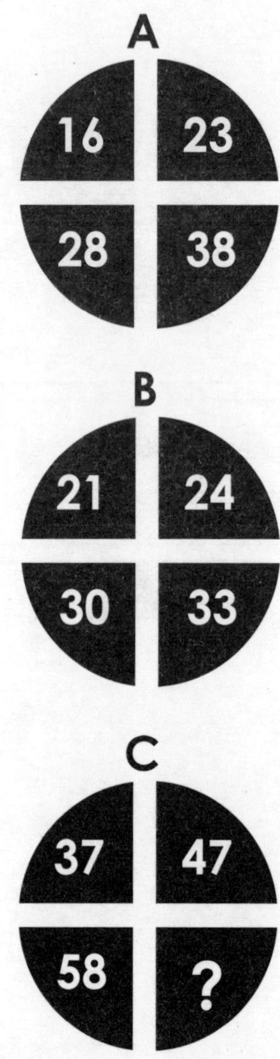

Add 21 to the missing value in this puzzle to find your next passcode.

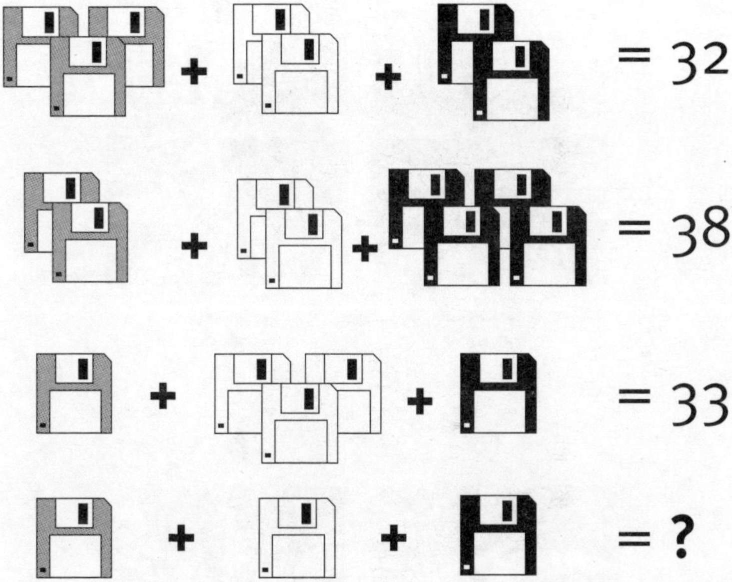

+ + = 32

+ + = 38

+ + = 33

+ + = ?

Pick the odd-one-out and use the number below it as your passcode to the next puzzle.

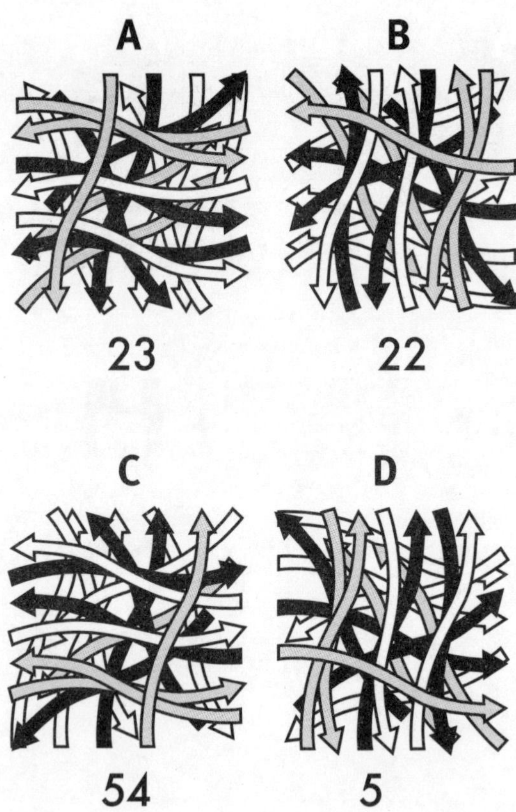

Continue the sequence and add 42 to the missing number to find your next passcode.

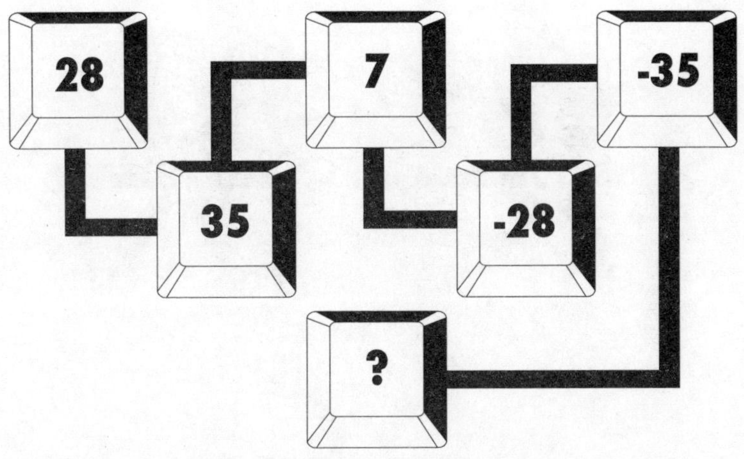

This is a test of your lateral thinking. Three times the missing number in C is your passcode to the next puzzle.

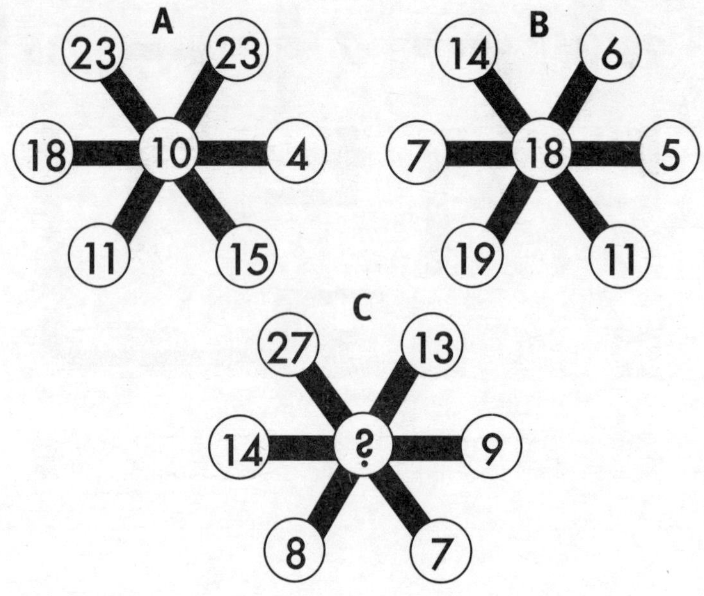

MIND MAZE M21

Put in the missing numbers in the shaded squares so that each black square is surrounded by 4 numbers that, multiplied together, make the number inside it. Deduct 21 from the total of the missing numbers added together to find your next passcode.

6		3		2		5		1		7		4		3
	90		120		80		90		189		336		384	
1														8
	90		320		192		378		945		60		160	
9														5
	324		384		192		126		840		60		60	
6														4
	90		840		448		96		192		144		324	
1		5		7		8		2		4		3		9

Add 27 to the missing number in C to find your next passcode on your tour of cyber-reality.

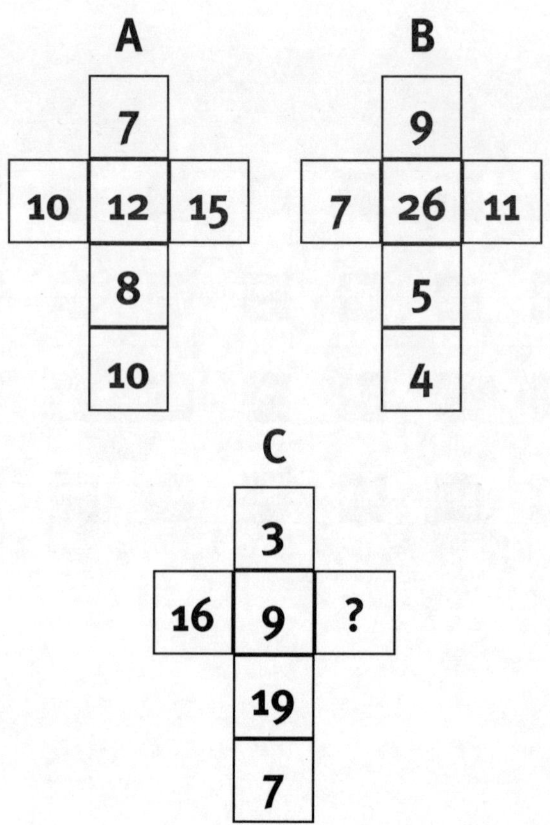

Something different! Add 41 to the missing number in D to find your next passcode.

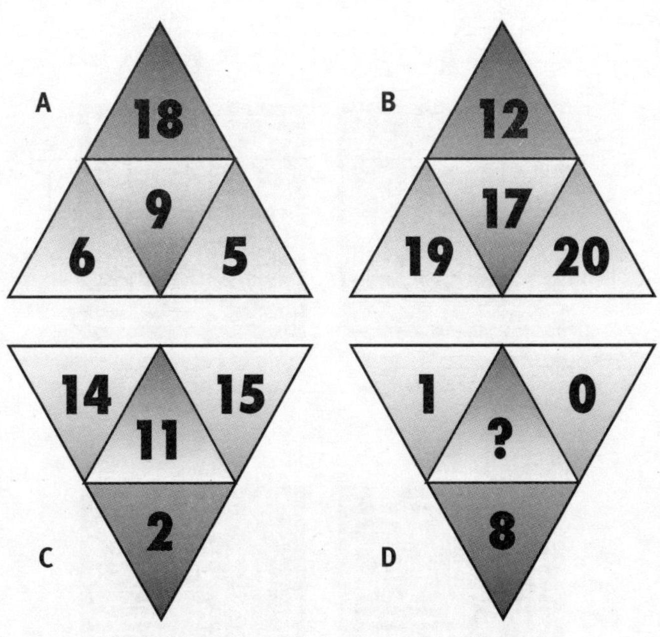

Pick the odd-one-out from these circuit sections, and choose your passcode accordingly. **A**=Passcode **15. B**=Passcode **33. C**=Passcode **47. D**=Passcode **10.**

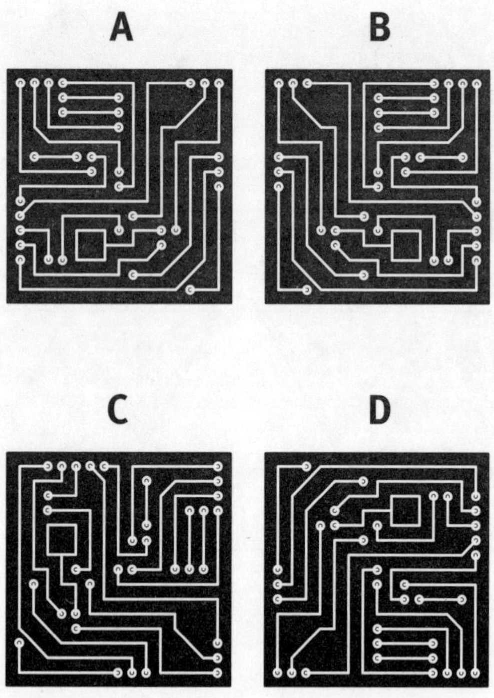

Add 22 to the missing number in this puzzle to get your next passcode.

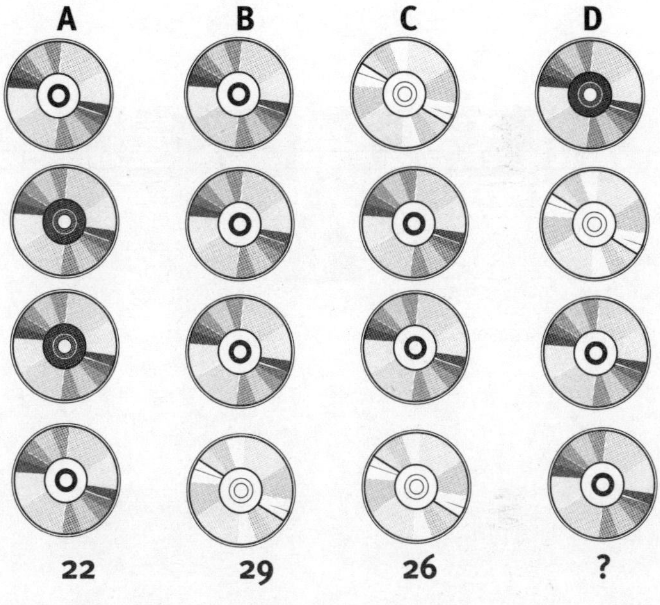

This system is in balance. Work out the missing value and add 34 to find your passcode to the next puzzle.

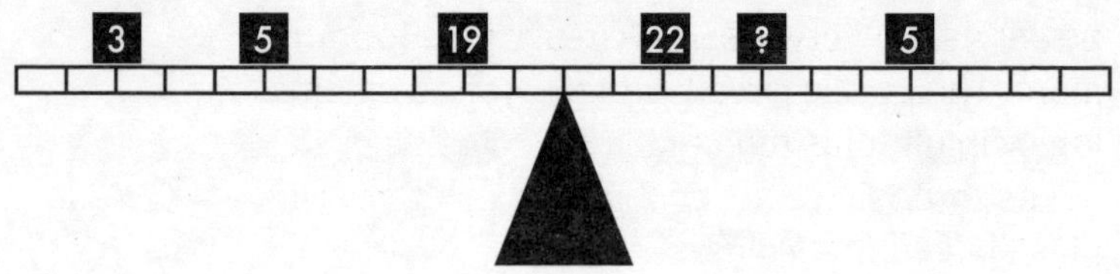

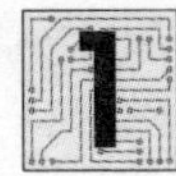

As a result of your success so far, four of the circuits in Adrian's processor network are competing for resources – the puzzle circuit, the maths circuit, the logic circuit and the nervousness circuit. The total pool of available interrupt power is currently set at 221 standard units.

The math circuit is demanding four times as much power as the nervousness circuit, plus four units more. The puzzle circuit wants twice as much as the logic circuit, plus ten units more. The logic circuit needs three times as much as the maths circuit, plus sixteen units more.

When you know how much power the logic circuit is drawing in standard units, subtract 3 and use that as your passcode to your next puzzle.

Add 45 to the missing number in D to find your next passcode.

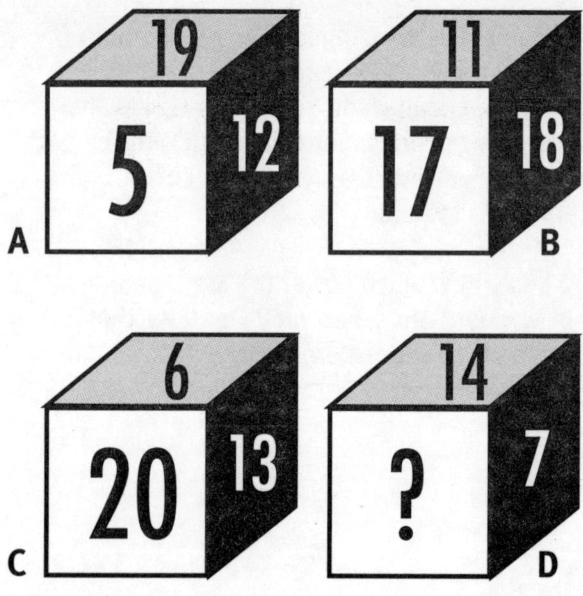

Multiply the missing number in C by 8 and add 2 to find the passcode to your next puzzle.

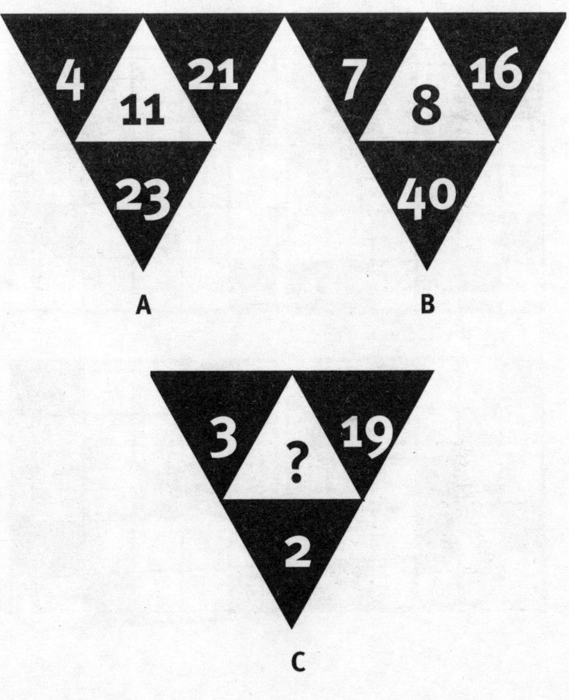

Pick the odd-one-out and choose your passcode accordingly. A=Passcode 10. B=Passcode 42. C=Passcode 17. D=Passcode 29.

The missing number in C is your next passcode.

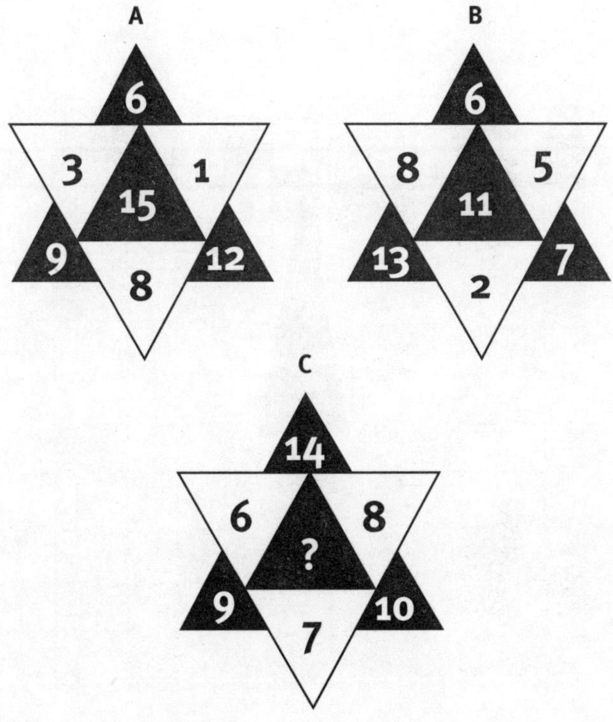

Deduct 5 from the value of the missing number in this puzzle to find your next passcode.

The missing number in this set is your next passcode.

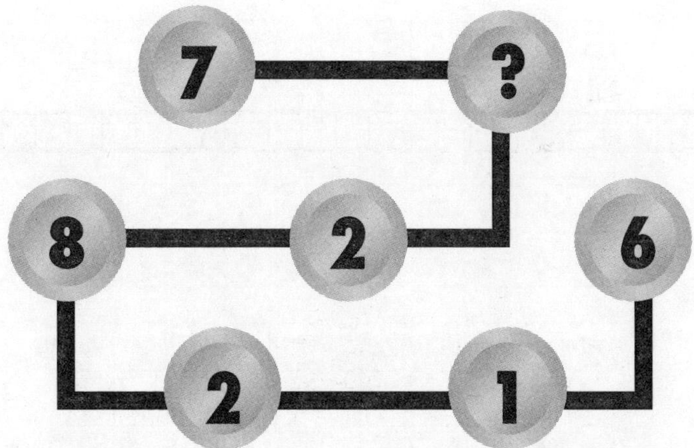

Find the missing digit in D and use that, with 10 added, as your next passcode.

A

3	1	6	2	8
5	9	2	8	4
2	6	5	0	3
1	8	4	3	5
4	0	1	6	2

B

7	8	1	3	5
1	4	5	4	7
3	5	7	6	0
0	4	3	5	1
4	3	2	1	9

C

2	8	4	9	7
3	6	2	1	5
5	3	9	0	8
4	2	0	5	2
1	5	3	4	0

D

3	8	6	7	5
4	1	4	3	6
0	5	4	1	7
2	6	1	5	3
6	4	3	3	?

Fill missing numbers in the shaded squares so that the digits surrounding each black square add to that number. Subtract 72 from the total of missing digits to find your next passcode.

7		9		3		5		8		4		2		6
	28		26		21		22		19		20		20	
4														3
	24		21		25		19		15		29		24	
8														4
	20		14		20		20		17		23		24	
3														9
	19		19		17		20		20		13		15	
6		5		7		2		8		3		2		1

Your next passcode is 5 less than the number that exactly balances the bottom set of scales.

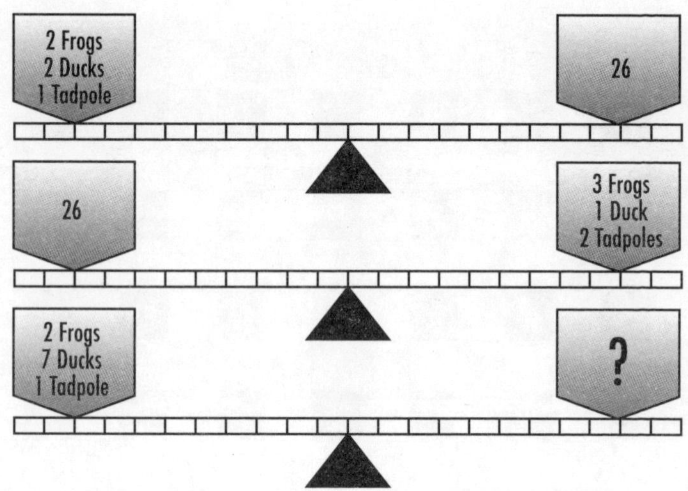

Multiply the missing number in C by 4 to find your next passcode.

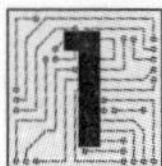

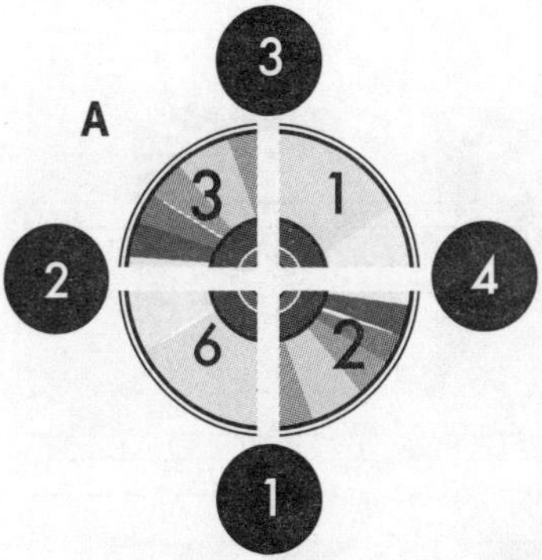

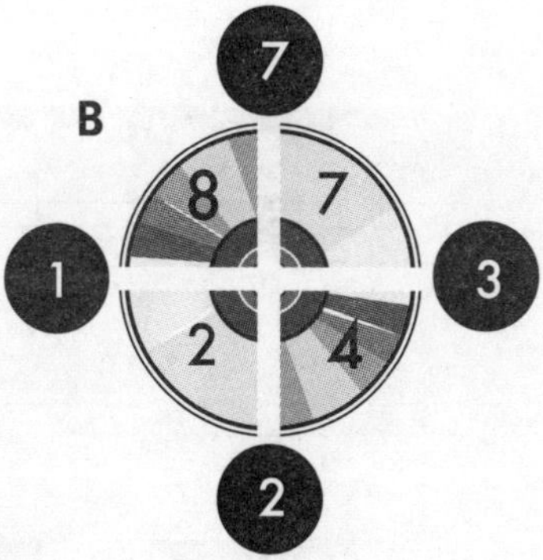

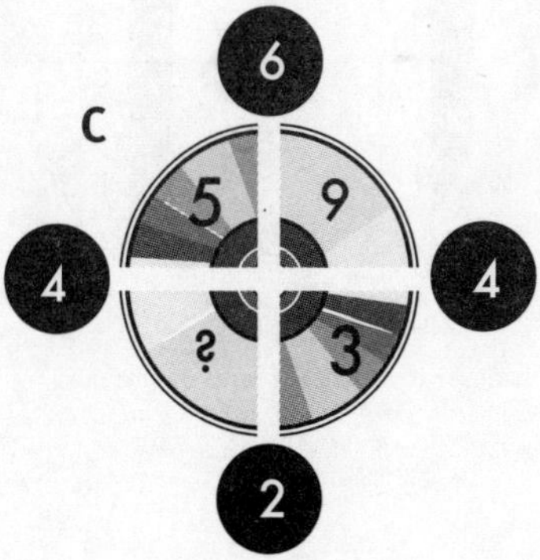

A: top 3, left 2, right 4, bottom 1; segments 3, 1, 6, 2

B: top 7, left 1, right 3, bottom 2; segments 8, 7, 2, 4

C: top 6, left 4, right 4, bottom 2; segments 5, 9, ?, 3

Continue the sequence (left to right) and deduct 34 from the missing number to find your next passcode.

What comes next: A, B, C or D? The number under the solution is your next passcode.

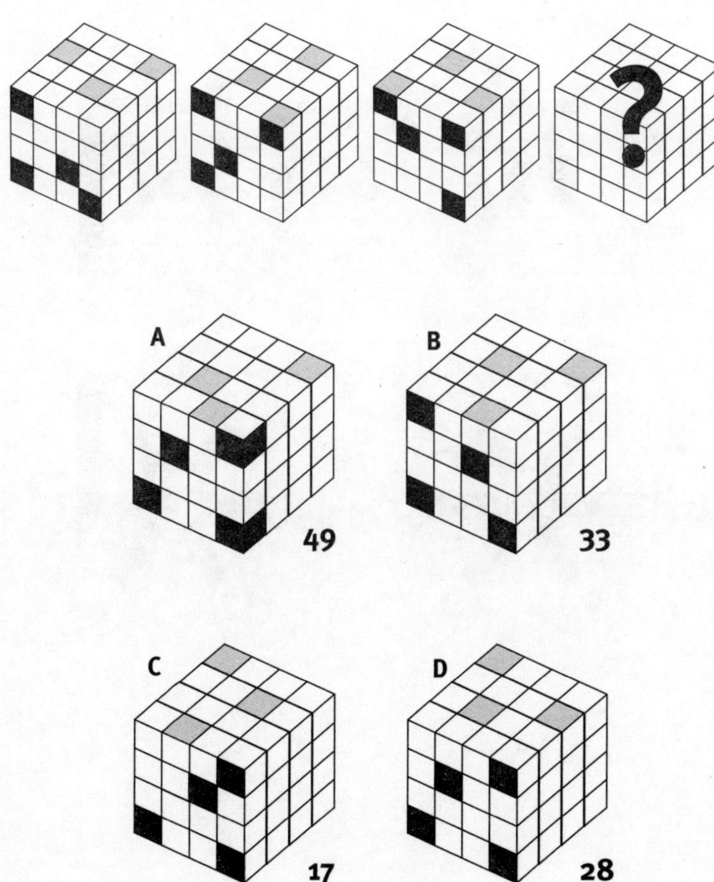

The solution to D is your next passcode.

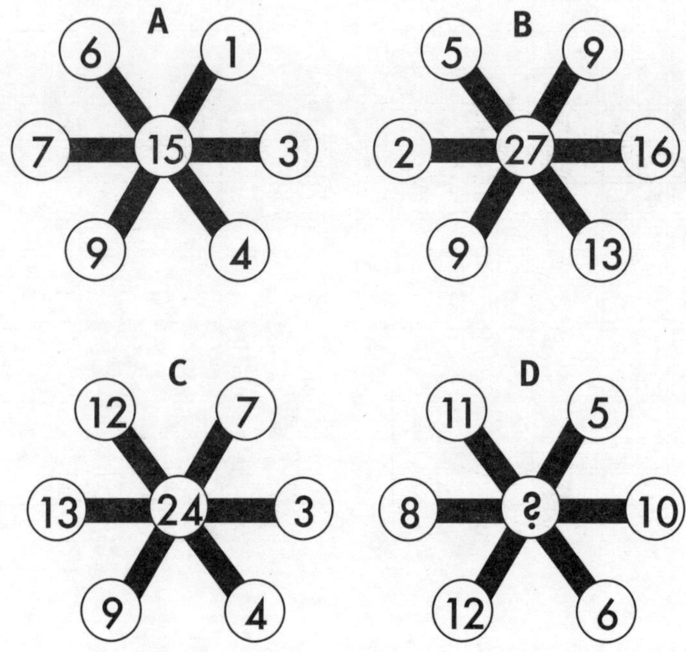

Subtract 2 from the number of differences between A & B to find your next passcode.

4			●				●		O
1		●			●				3
9		B		●	2	9	1	●	6
2		●			A		●		8
●		X		●				O	●
	●			\					
B			●		●			\	
R	●	O	C	Y	M			●	●
●				●					O
	↓	●			●	Z	A		●
●	O	D		X		K	●		
			●			K		/	\
	●	O				●			↑
	→			●			●		
/		●	2	3	O	●			O

4			●				●		O
1		●			●				3
9		B		●	2	9	1	●	6
2		●			A		●		8
●		X		●				O	●
	●			/		●			
R			●		●			\	
B	●	O	C	Y	M			●	●
●				●					O
	↑	●			●	Z	A		●
●	O	D		X		V	●		
			●			K		/	/
	●	O				●			↑
	→			●			●		
/		●	2	3	O	●			O

What comes next? Choose your passcode accordingly.
A=Passcode **13.** **B**=Passcode **29.** **C**=Passcode **8.**
D=Passcode **48.**

Your next passcode on your escape-route from cyber-reality is the missing value in D.

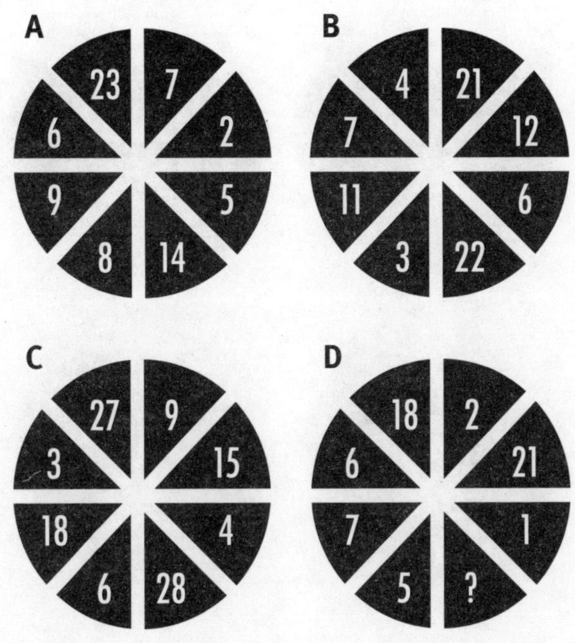

Deduct 29 from the missing value in D to find the passcode to the next puzzle in your quest.

Pick the odd-one-out and use the number above it as your next passcode.

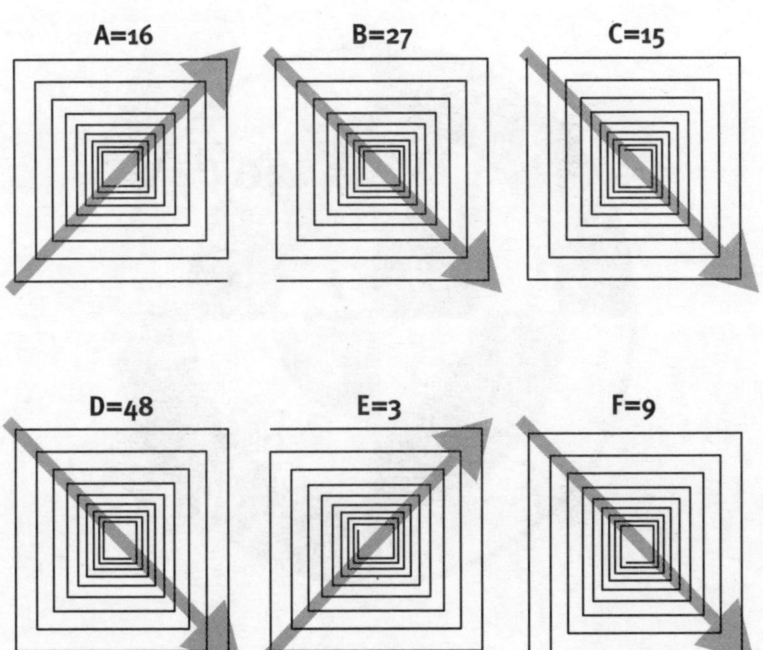

Subtract 7 from the missing number in this puzzle to find your next passcode.

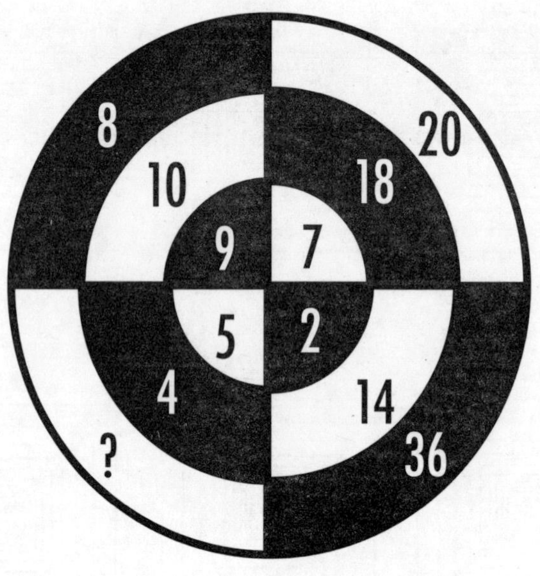

Use the first digit of the solution to this puzzle as your next passcode.

11980	is to	57	as	32613	is to	45
25674	is to	72	as	44557	is to	?

A	B	C	D
46	75	15	33

Add 14 to the solution to this puzzle to find your next passcode.

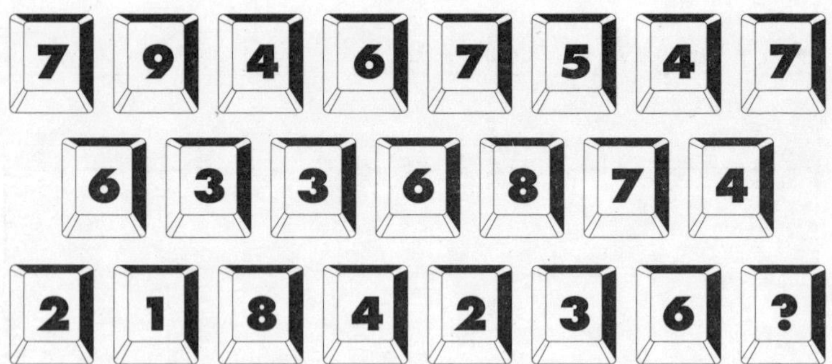

Fill out the missing numbers in this square using only the digits already supplied so that you make a magic square with each row, column and long diagonal totalling 27. When you have done that, subtract 93 from the total of all the missing digits to find your next passcode.

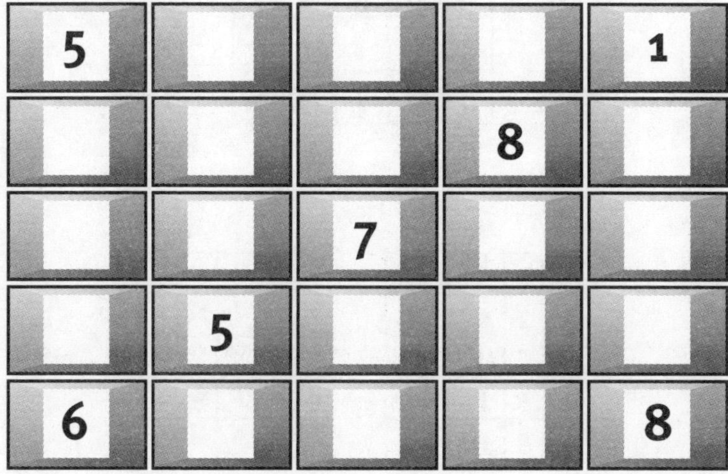

Pick the odd-one-out from A, B, C and D, compared to the example box immediately below, and use the number below it as your next passcode.

5	B	A	X	3
9	2	4	Z	K
B	G	H	4	7
L	5	J	M	R
2	P	I	O	N

A

5	B	A	X	3
9	2	4	Z	K
7	4	H	G	B
L	5	J	M	R
N	O	I	P	2

10

B

2	P	I	O	N
L	5	J	M	R
7	4	H	G	B
K	Z	4	2	9
3	X	A	B	5

43

C

N	R	B	K	5
O	M	G	Z	B
I	J	H	4	A
P	5	4	2	X
2	L	7	9	3

14

D

5	K	7	R	2
B	Z	4	M	P
A	4	H	J	I
X	2	G	5	O
3	9	B	L	N

59

Complete the analogy and use the number below it as your next passcode.

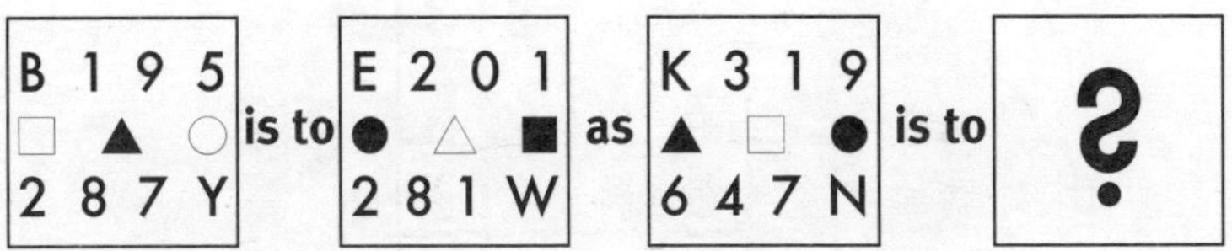

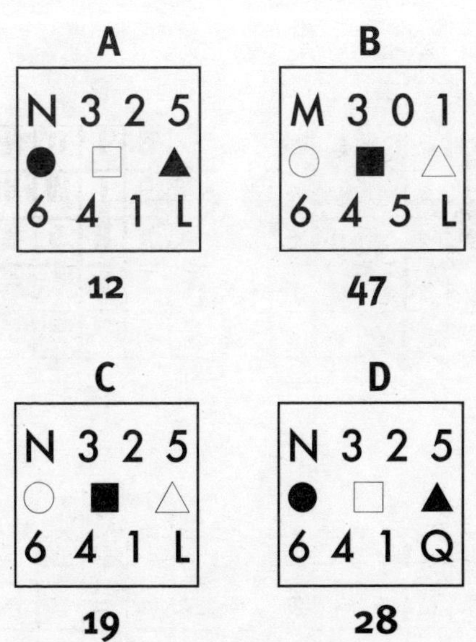

Subtract 20 from the missing number in this set to find your passcode to the next puzzle.

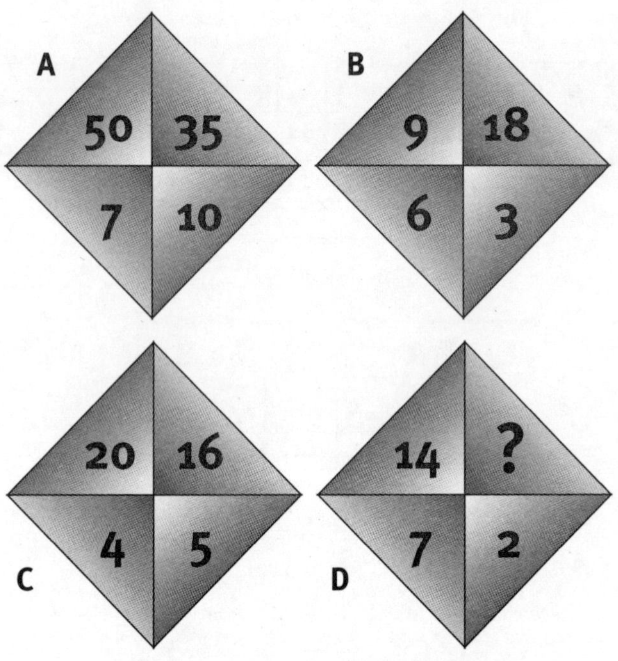

Pick the odd-one-out from these four examples. The middle number, plus 6, is your next passcode.

A

5	8	9	2	9
4	2	6	1	5
1	5	3	7	1
8	7	2	6	4
4	6	3	5	8

B

4	5	7	9	2
2	9	5	6	8
8	0	8	3	9
3	7	1	0	2
1	6	2	4	3

C

6	1	7	0	3
3	0	4	8	5
7	8	5	2	1
2	1	4	9	2
7	6	5	3	4

D

7	3	8	9	5
0	2	6	1	2
9	8	9	3	4
7	3	4	0	3
8	1	6	4	6

Solve for A, B & C to find your next passcode.

A	A	A	A	
A	B	A	B	A
B	B	A	C	B
B	B	B	C	C
C	C	C	C	?
36	38	34	28	

This is a test of lateral numerical reasoning. The missing number in C is your next passcode.

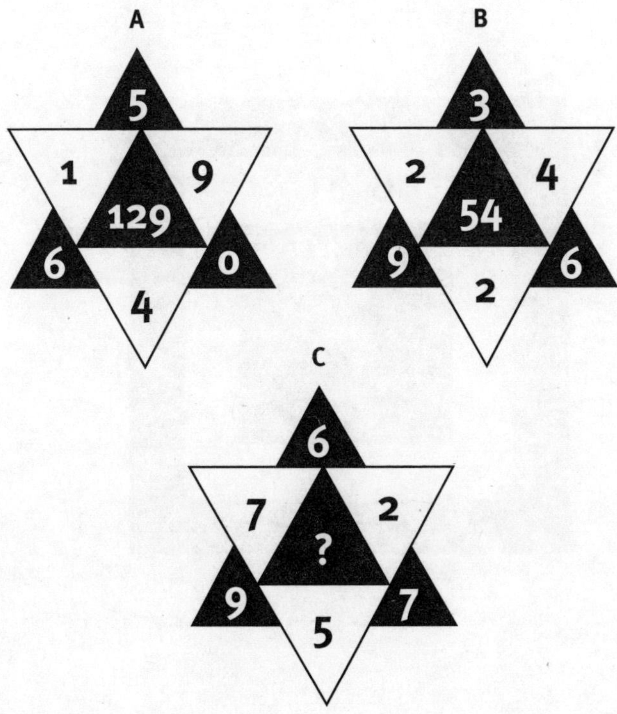

This symmetrical figure is divided into 3 zones, A, B & C. The number inside the zone which covers most area is your next passcode, and is not part of the puzzle.

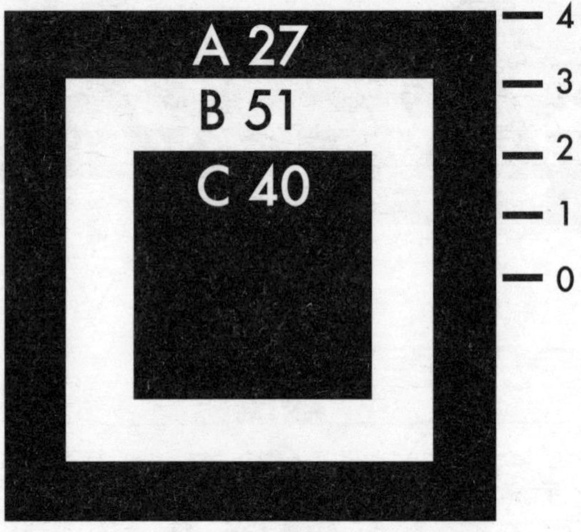

Pick the odd-one-out and find your next passcode accordingly.

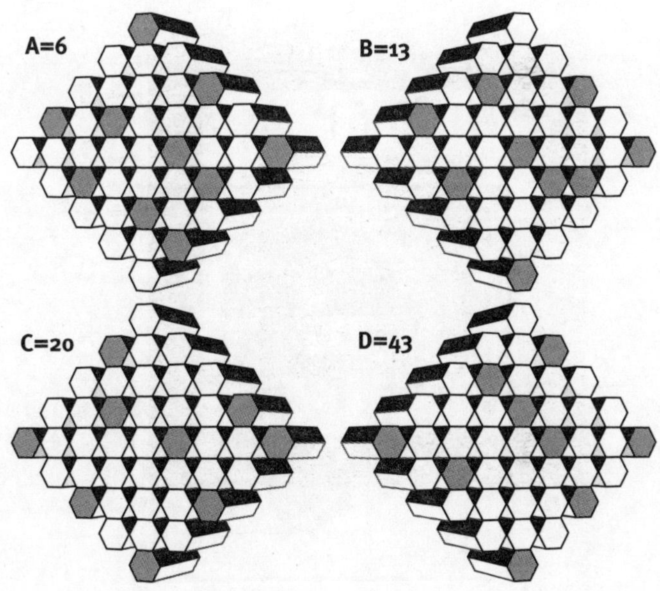

Your next passcode is the number that, when you add 6 to it and double the result, gives you the number that, when you add 42, produces a number that equals the square of the value of the roman numeral whose alphabetical position is one greater than the number you are seeking.

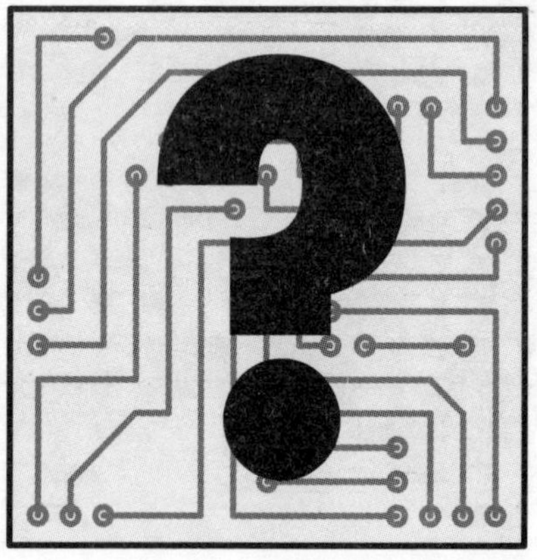

What is the missing number, A, B, C or D? Choose your passcode accordingly. **A**=Passcode 25. **B**=Passcode 27. **C**=Passcode 44. **D**=Passcode 31.

A

B

C

D

Pick the odd-one-out and use it as your passcode to the next puzzle.

KEYCODES

REMINDER: You must solve the puzzles in the correct order. Start at the top of column A in the chart on the next page, and insert your keys. When you get to the bottom of column A, start back at the top of column B.

Subtract the total of column A from the total of column B. The result is your Passcode. If you have entered the keys correctly, your passcode will match the figure in the Passcode box.

Adrian Smith is angry that you have reached this stage of the book. He thought you would have given up long ago. Who do you think you are?

Total A

Total B

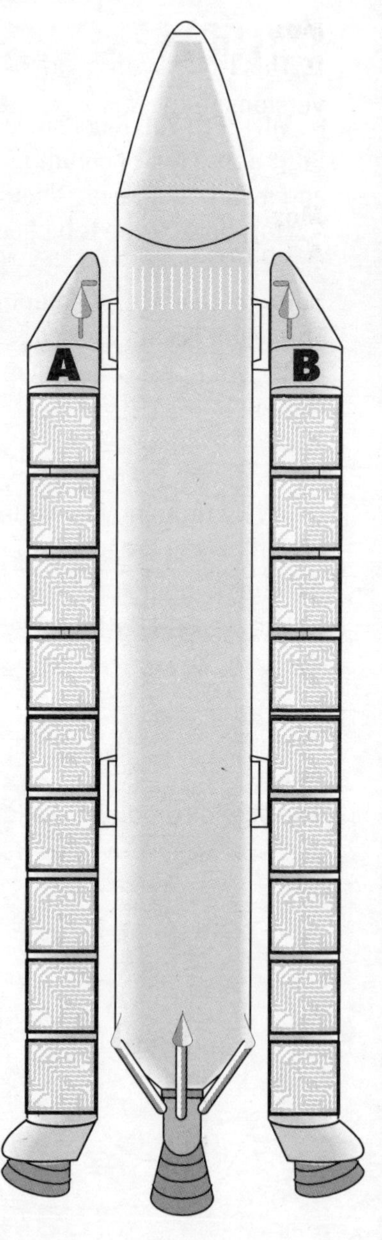

6

PASSCODE

M01

D. This is a mirror-image of the others which are all rotated versions of the same puzzle. Go to 49. Key 2.

M02

A. Go to 50.

M03

A. Row 1: 4x3=6+6; Row 2: 4x4=8+8; Row 3: 4x5=8+8+4. Hence Row 4: 4x6=8+4+8+4. Go to 47.

M04

31. The numbers on either side of each set add to the same as the top and bottom numbers multiplied together.
Go to 31. Key 3.

M05

The shape containing 43 does not fit. Go to 43.

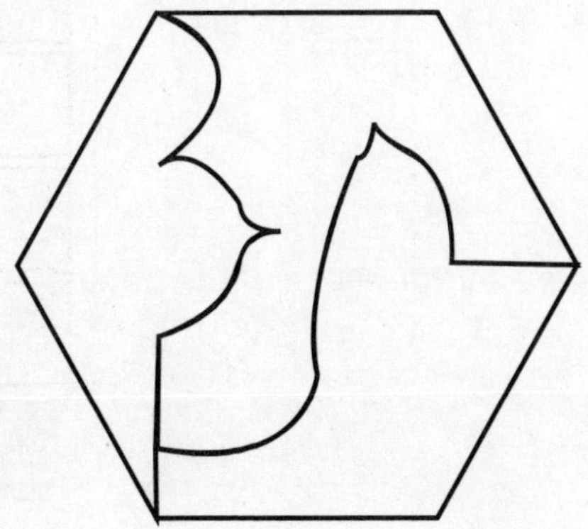

M06

B. The circled cross has changed shade. The other shapes are all rotated versions of the same puzzle. Go to 48.

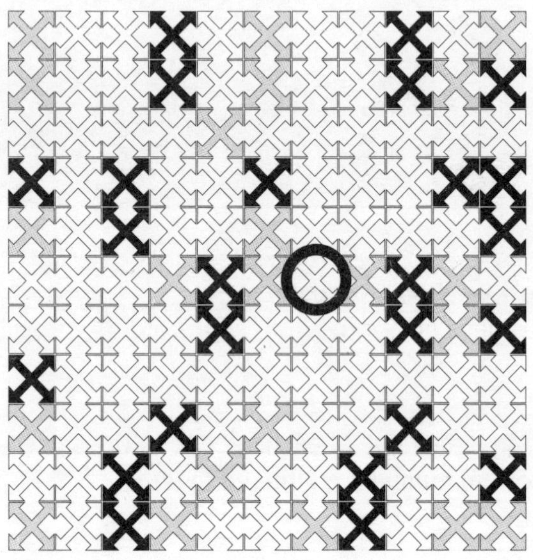

M07

52. The missing number is 13. The inner numbers add to the same as the outer numbers in each set. 4x13=52. Go to 52. Key 4.

M08

C is the odd-one-out. This is a mirror-image of the others, which are all rotated versions of the same thing. The correct figure is shown below. Go to 34.

M09

51. The sum 52-31=21. The values are shown below. Go to 51.

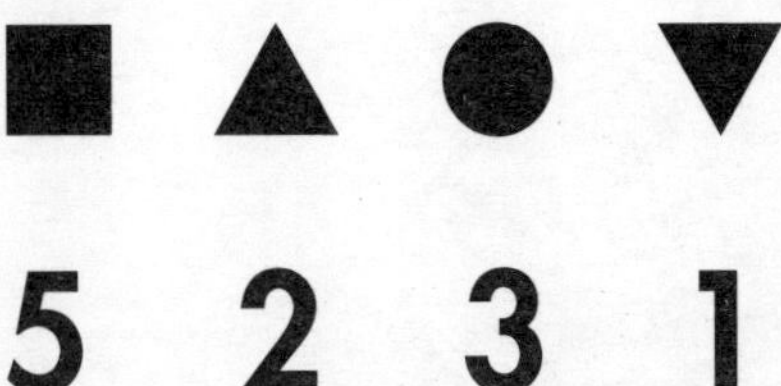

M10

A. An extra dot has been placed in A. The others are all rotated versions. Go to 39.

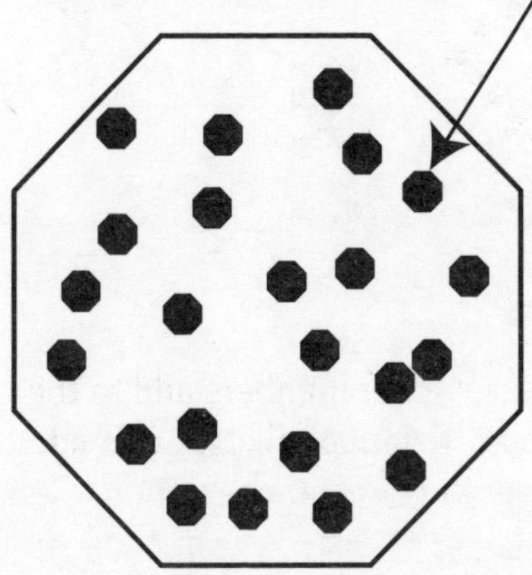

M11

41. The missing number is 4. In each big triangle, top number x middle number = half the number formed from the bottom 2 digits. In C, 6x7=42; 2x42=8[4]. 4+37=41. Go to 41. Key 3.

M12

37. There are 7 differences, as circled below. 7+30=37.
Go to 37.

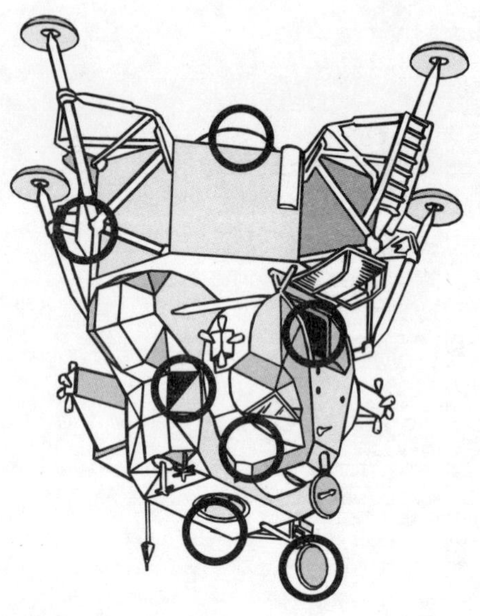

M13

45. The missing number is 12. With double digits, add both digits together and add 2 to get the next number. Thus, 2+8=10, 10+2=[12]; 1+2=3, 3+2=5; 5+2=7; 7+2=9; 9+2=11; 1+1=2, 2+2=4; 4+2=6. 12X4=48; 48-3=45. Go to 45.

M14

B. The circled spot below has changed shade. The other shapes are all rotated versions of the same drawing. Go to 59.

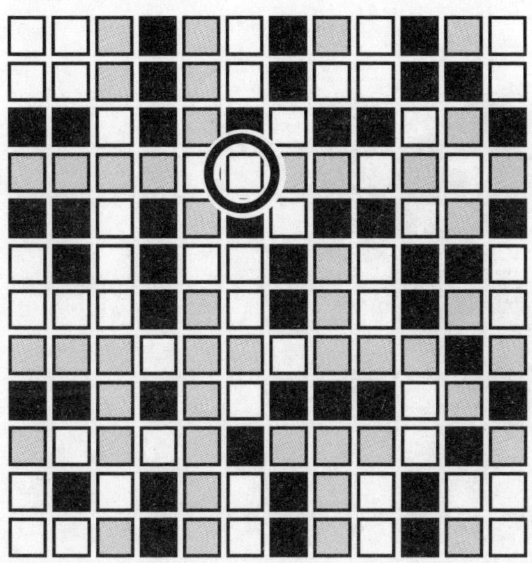

M15

32. Dogs=7; Cats=4; Mice=3. Go to 32. Key 1.

M16

55. The missing number is 71. Referring to the diagram below, in each example, A+(both digits of A added together) =B; B+(both digits of B added together)=C; C+(both digits of C added together)=D. 71-16=55. Go to 55.

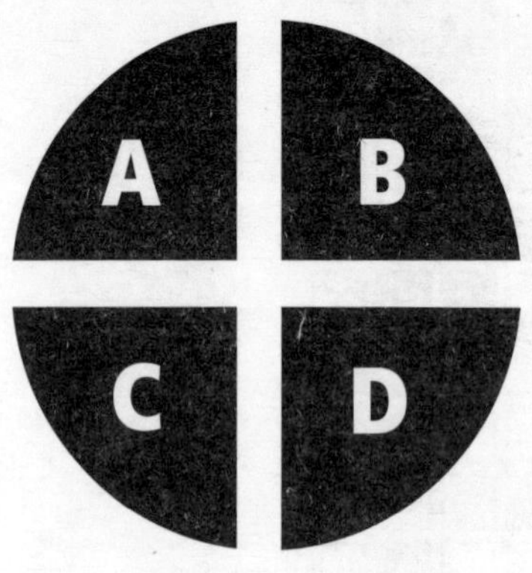

M17

36. The missing value is 15. Component values are shown below. 21+15=36. Go to 36.

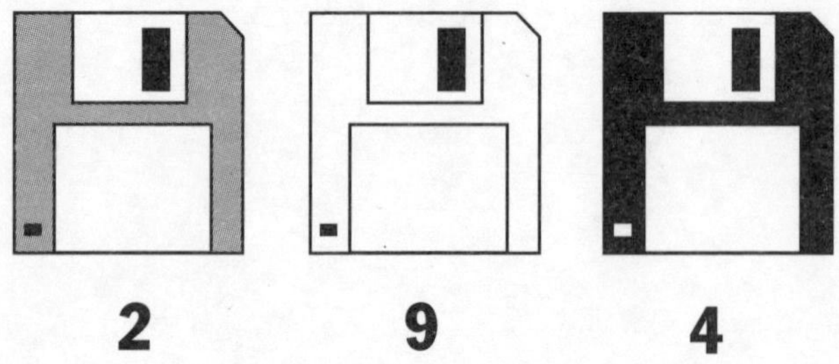

M18

C is the odd-one-out. The line pointed to here has changed colour in C. Go to 54.

M19

35. For each number, take the number before it from it, to give the number following it. 35-28 = 7; 7-35 = -28; -28-7 = -35; -35-(-28) = -7. -7+42 = 35. Go to 35. Key 5.

M20

60. The missing number is 20. In each set, referring to the example, (A+B+C)-(D+E+F)=G. 3x20=60. Go to 60.

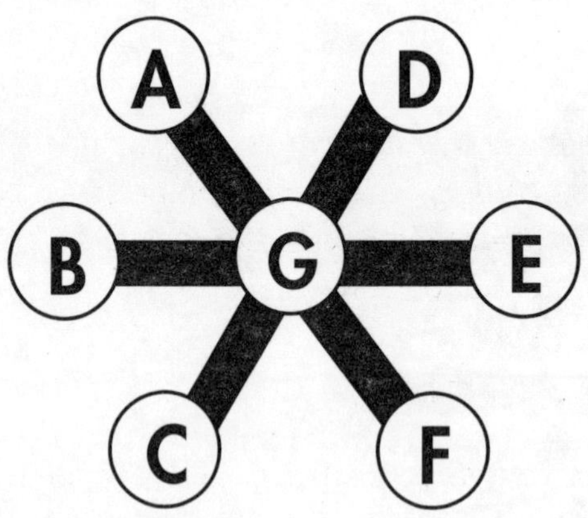

M21

57. The total of the missing numbers, referring to the diagram below, is 78. 78-21=57. Go to 57.

6		3		2		5		1		7		4		3
	90		120		80		90		189		336		384	
1		5		4		2		9		3		4		8
	90		320		192		378		945		60		160	
9		2		8		3		7		5		1		5
	324		384		192		126		840		60		60	
6		3		8		1		6		4		3		4
	90		840		448		96		192		144		324	
1		5		7		8		2		4		3		9

M22

40. The missing number is 13. The vertical numbers add to the same as the horizontal numbers in each cross. Go to 40.

M23

44. The missing number is 3. The number in each small triangle in large triangles A or B + the number in the same position below it in C or D = 20. Thus in D, the central 17 from B + [3]=20. 41+3=44. Go to 44. Key 6.

M24

B. This is a mirror-image of the others, which are all rotated versions of the same puzzle. Go to 33.

M25

46. The missing number is 24. The values are shown below. 24+22=46. Go to 46.

M26

38. The missing value is 4. On either side, multiply each block's numerical position from the middle by its weight, and add the results to find the total weight on either side. On the left, (19x2 =38)+(5x6=30)+(3x9=27)=95; on the right, (22x2 =44)+(5x7=35)+([4]x4=16)=95. Thus the system is balanced. 4+34=38. Go to 38.

M27

61. The nervousness circuit is drawing 3 units, the maths circuit is drawing 16 units, the logic circuit is drawing 64 units, and the puzzle circuit is drawing 138 units. 64-3=61. Congratulations! You've finished.

M28

53. The missing number is 8. The total of the tops of all the cubes is the same as the total of the sides and thus, logically, the fronts. Hence, 5+17+20+[8]=50. 45+8=53. Go to 53.

M29

58. The missing number is 7. Referring to the diagram below, in each large triangle, C+D divided by A=B. Thus, in C, (19+2)/ 3=7. 7x8=56; 56+2=8. Go to 58.

M30

B. This is a mirror-image of the others, which are all rotated versions of the same pattern. Go to 42. Key 7.

M31

12. In each case, total of numbers in the back triangle – total of numbers in the front triangle = the number in the middle. Go to 12.

M32

3. The missing number is 8. There is a total distance x weight value of 48 on the left; hence we need to balance that on the right. Since the box is at position 6 we need 6x[8]=48. 8-5=3. Go to 3.

M33

4. The sequence is 7x[4]=28; 8x2=16, reusing the 8. Go to 4.

M34

11. In each set, the columns add to the same: 15, 24, 18, 19 and 22 from left to right. Thus 5+6+7+3+[1]=22. 1+10=11. Go to 11. Key 3.

M35

22. Referring to the diagram below, the missing digits total 94. 94-72=22. Go to 22.

7		9		3		5		8		4		2		6
	28		26		21		22		19		20		20	
4		8		6		7		2		5		9		3
	24		21		25		19		15		29		24	
8		4		3		9		1		7		8		4
	20		14		20		20		17		23		24	
3		5		2		6		4		5		3		9
	19		19		17		20		20		13		15	
6		5		7		2		8		3		2		1

M36

61-5=56. Frogs=5; Ducks=7; Tadpoles=2. Go to 56. Key 4.

M37

28. On the outside numbers, the top number x the right digit = the bottom and left digits. Thus in C, 6x4=24. The inner numbers total to the multiplication result. Thus in C, 5+9+3+[7]=24. 4x7=28. Go to 28. Key 1.

M38

8. The missing number is 42. The sequence is a series of subtractions, reducing by 1 with each step. Thus, 72-8=64; 64-7=57; 57-6=51; 51-5=46; 46-4=42. 42-34=8. Go to 8.

M39

C. The top and the front independently rotate 90° clockwise each step. Go to 17.

M40

26. The central number in each set is half the sum of all the surrounding numbers. Go to 26.

M41

5. There are 7 differences. 7-2=5. Differences: 5th line up V/K; 6th line down, line changes direction, extra spot; 7th/8th line down, B/R and R/B; 4th line up, line changes direction; 6th line up, down arrow/up arrow. Go to 5. Key 3.

M42

A. In each circle, the sum of the bottom numbers should be 2 less than the sum of the top numbers. Only A fits this condition. Go to 13.

M43

24. Divide each circle diagonally from top left to bottom right. The sums in each of the diagonal halves are equal. Go to 24.

M44

10. The missing number is 39. The sum of the surrounding numbers in each example, plus 8 = the central number. 39-29=10. Go to 10.

M45

F. In every other example with a clockwise spiral, the arrow points up. Go to 9.

M46

21. The missing number is 28. 28-7=21. In each case, the numbers in the next outward ring are double their counterparts in the previous, inner, ring. Thus, 7 doubles to 14 and again to 28. Go to 21.

M47

B. The analogy is for the sum of the digits in the larger box, times three. Thus 4+4+5+5+7=25; 25x3=75. Use the 7. Go to 7.

M48

18. The missing number is 4. 4+14=18. Each central number, added to the 2 numbers above and the 2 numbers below = 25. Thus, 4+7+4+6+[4]=25. Go to 18. Key 4.

M49

2. The sum of all the missing digits, as below, is 95. 95-93=2. Go to 2.

5	8	6	7	1
7	1	5	8	6
8	6	7	1	5
1	5	8	6	7
6	7	1	5	8

M50

C. This is the only set with 3 lines reversed compared to the example in the box. Go to 14. Key 0.

M51

C. The top letter gains 3 alphabetic places; the top number gains 6; the middle symbols reverse and the colours reverse; the bottom number loses 6 and the bottom letter loses 2 alphabetic places. Go to 19.

M52

29. The missing number is 49. In each example, divide the lower of each of the diametrically opposite numbers into the higher number to achieve the same result. For example, in C, 20/5=16/4; in D, 14/2=49/[7]. Thus, 49-20=29. Go to 29. Key 8.

M53

D. In each of the others, both long diagonals add to 24, but in D, the lower left to top right diagonal adds to 26. 9+6=15. Go to 15.

M54

20. A=7; B=9; C=4. Go to 20.

M55

30. Referring to the star below, ABC-DEF=G. Thus, 627-597=30. Go to 30.

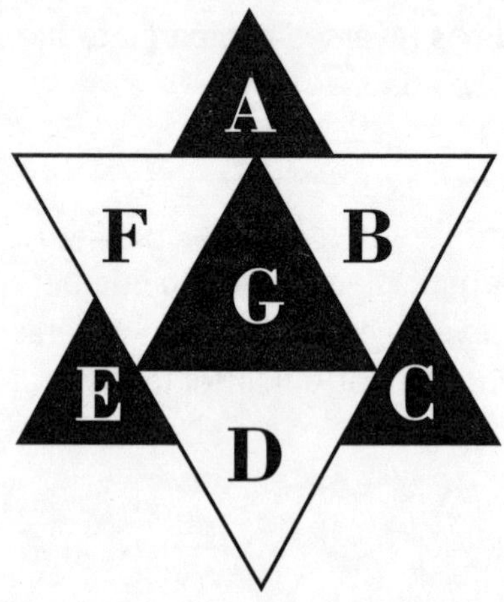

M56

27. Solution A. A has an area of 28 square units, B has an area of 20 square units and C has an area of 16 square units. A is therefore the largest. Go to 27. Key 7.

M57

A. All the others have 9 dark hexagons, but A has 10. Go to 6.

M58

23. (23+6)x2=58; 58+42=100. X is the Roman numeral for 10; 10x10=100. X is the 24th (23+1) letter of the alphabet. Go to 23.

M59

A. The top numbers are the result of subtracting the reverse of the bottom numbers from 100,000. Hence, 100,000-96,582=3,418. Go to 25.

M60

16. This is the only perfect square of a perfect square (4) present. The others are only perfect squares. Go to 16. Key 2.

ANSWERS 1–92

Puzzle 1

1 Kentucky.

2 Rhode Island.

3 The Mississippi.

4 1787.

5 The Congress.

6 Thirteen.

7 California.

8 St. Augustine, Florida.

9 Andrew Jackson.

10 The Senate and The House of Representatives.

11 New York, Los Angeles and Chicago.

12 Tallahassee.

13 The Seminole War.

14 In the south-west, in particular New Mexico and Arizona.

15 The annexation of Texas by the USA in 1845.

16 The Confederacy.

17 The Republicans.

18 Two four-year terms.

19 Thirty-five.

20 Augusta.

21 Lyndon B. Johnson.

22 Washington.

23 Ross Perot.

24 New Deal.

25 The Potomac.

26 Mardi Gras.

27 The Star-spangled Banner.

28 Juneau.

29 The Apaches.

30 The Mississippi.

Puzzle 2

C. It is the only one which does not have half as many 'step' lines as there are triangles.

Puzzle 3

E. The shape has been folded along a horizontal line. A shaded piece covers an unshaded one.

Puzzle 4

QUS 2321. For each plate, go forward by 4 and back by 2 in the alphabet to get the 2nd and 3rd letters, then continue this pattern but use numbers representing the letters' alphabetical position.

Puzzle 5

Degas. Each letter is the same number of letters from the end of the alphabet as the letter in the artist's name is from the beginning.

Puzzle 6

The corresponding sections in each wheel should contain a black section in each compartment.

Puzzle 7

B. The digits of all the others add up to 6.

Puzzle 8

+ ÷ – x – +. The letters are based on their alphabetic position, so the sum would read: L(12) + D(4) ÷ B(2) – F(6) x K(11) – Q(17) + C(3) = H(8).

Puzzle 9

G. Add 3 to odd numbers, subtract 2 from even numbers.

Puzzle 10

Kebab, Pasta, Pizza, Tacos, Wurst.

Puzzle 11

The pattern sequence is 7, 1, 1, 3, 2, 2, 5, 5, 4, 1. It starts at the top right and works in an anti-clockwise spiral.

4	2	2
1	5	5
7	1	1

Puzzle 12

The pattern sequence is @, @, %, *, %, &, &, *, %. It starts at the top right and works inwards in an anti-clockwise spiral.

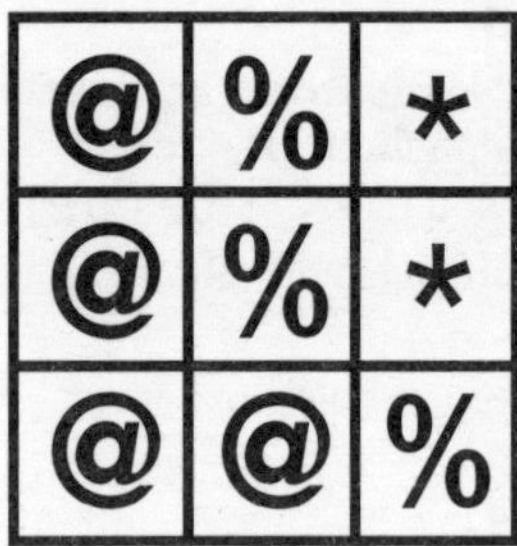

Puzzle 13

384. Starting at the top right hand corner work through the square in a vertical boustrophedon, multiplying by 4 and dividing by 2 alternately.

Puzzle 14

1 Ian Fleming.

2 Leonardo da Vinci.

3 The Republicans.

4 The Spanish Steps.

5 Cricket.

6 Benazir Bhutto.

7 The Chinese Communist party.

8 The Middle Kingdom.

9 Queensland and Northern Territories Air Service.

10 Lake Victoria.

11 Sri Lanka.

12 Lion.

13 The Indian subcontinent.

14 Cambridge.

15 Multiple sclerosis.

16 Thomas Hardy.

17 The kidneys.

18 Bile.

19 The lawn mower.

20 The first monument of this kind was built at Halicarnassus to house the body of Mausolus.

21 Tsars and Tsarinas.

22 A surface-to-air-missile.

23 Japan.

24 Ezra Pound.

25 The Central Criminal Court.

26 Mark Chapman.

27 Lynette (Squeaky) Fromm.

28 Richard Nixon.

29 Someone who deputizes for a doctor or clergyman.

30 A dance.

31 Wallis Simpson.

32 Laos.

33 Republic of Ireland.

34 Scarlett O'Hara in *Gone With the Wind*.

35 Gaelic.

36 Joseph Heller.

37 1967.

38 West.

39 *The Godfather.*

40 Eeyore.

41 A funeral rite or ceremony.

42 Ruth Ellis.

43 1914.

44 Country and western.

45 Ernest Hemingway.

46 *Breakfast at Tiffany's*; Capote wrote the novel, Hepburn played the lead in the film.

47 Every four years.

48 Undertaker and mortician.

49 *Cul* is a vulgar word for buttocks.

50 Goolagong.

Puzzle 15

G. It is a term for tempo, while the others are types of dances.

Puzzle 16

Yes. Swansea had no O in it.

Puzzle 17

V. The letters are based on the number alphabet backwards (Z = 1, A = 26, etc). The values on the bottom corners and the value in the middle added together result in the value on the apex.

Puzzle 18

Bodega, Bonsai, Ersatz, Hombre, Kitsch.

Puzzle 19

Fresno. Skip two letters in the alphabet each time.

Puzzle 20

C. Divide the left number by 2, place this number at the apex, then square it and put this number at the right. Finally, add all three numbers together and put the sum as a roman numeral in the middle. In triangle C, the right number should be 4 and the middle number should be X.

Puzzle 21

The faces pattern sequence is smiley, smiley, straight, sad, sad, smiley, straight, straight, sad, etc. Start at the bottom left and work in a horizontal boustrophedon.

Puzzle 22

F. Circles and rectangles interchange except for strings of 3 circles which disappear.

Puzzle 23

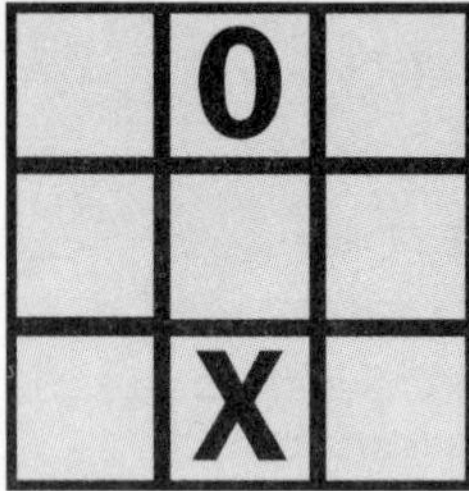

Starting at opposite ends the symbols move alternately 1 and 2 steps to the other end of the grid in a boustrophedon.

Puzzle 25

73235226252257. The numbers are in code from the newspaper titles. A–C = 1, D–F = 2, G–I = 3, J–L = 4, M–O = 5, P–R = 6 S–U = 7, V–X = 8, Y–Z = 9.

Puzzle 26

29. Add together the corner squares of each row or column in a clockwise direction. Put the sum in the middle of the next row or column.

Puzzle 24

S	E	R	E	P	E	N	S	T	I	N	E	R	E	S	E
E	E	S	E	N	R	P	E	N	S	E	R	P	E	N	T
R	S	R	S	E	I	S	R	T	E	R	P	E	N	T	I
P	E	P	P	S	E	T	P	I	N	E	N	E	S	S	S
E	R	E	S	N	T	N	N	N	E	R	I	N	N	N	E
N	P	N	E	R	T	E	T	E	P	N	S	E	E	I	R
T	E	T	R	P	S	I	I	T	P	T	P	T	R	T	P
N	N	I	P	E	E	N	N	T	R	R	S	E	P	N	E
E	T	N	E	N	T	E	E	E	E	S	E	T	E	E	N
I	N	E	N	T	R	S	E	S	R	E	T	S	N	P	T
S	E	R	T	P	E	N	T	I	N	E	T	S	T	R	I
S	E	R	N	P	E	N	T	I	N	E	E	N	I	E	T
E	S	R	E	I	S	E	R	P	E	N	T	I	N	S	E
S	E	T	E	N	N	I	T	N	E	P	R	E	S	T	E
R	S	E	N	E	I	T	N	I	P	R	E	S	E	S	T
S	E	R	P	E	N	S	N	I	T	N	E	P	R	E	S

Puzzle 27

1 Parmesan cheese.
2 A pepper.
3 Swede.
4 Seaweed.
5 A large shrimp.
6 Sicily.
7 A cheese.
8 A fool.
9 Fermented rice.
10 Pimento.
11 Sundae.
12 A ragout of meat or fish.
13 Egg yolk, oil, and lemon juice or vinegar.
14 A thick, sweetened and flavoured milk pudding.
15 A cream sauce with peppers and mushrooms.
16 Avocado.
17 Barley.
18 Chilli.
19 Brandy and gin.
20 Sour cream.
21 A mushroom, grown in eastern Asia.
22 Nutmeg.
23 Sausagemeat and breadcrumbs.
24 Egg whites and sugar.
25 Caraway seed.
26 A cake.
27 Pâté and pastry.
28 Stewed fruit or cheese rolled up in a thin layer of pastry and baked.
29 You fry them lightly in an open pan, tossing them occasionally.
30 Avocado.
31 Orange peel.
32 A savoury pastry.
33 Béchamel sauce.
34 A sort of relish.
35 Rum, creamed coconut and pineapple juice.
36 Belgium.
37 The bouquet.
38 It contains spinach.
39 Tarragon and chervil.
40 A curry.
41 Chocolate.
42 Blackcurrants.
43 Japan.
44 Hollandaise sauce.
45 A roux.
46 A sherry.
47 The pancreas.
48 Chinese cooking.
49 Peanut sauce.
50 The small intestines.

Puzzle 28

M. These are all the letters with straight sides only.

Puzzle 29

N. Going from the top to the bottom of one domino piece, then to the top of the next piece, etc., alternately move on five letters and three back.

Puzzle 30

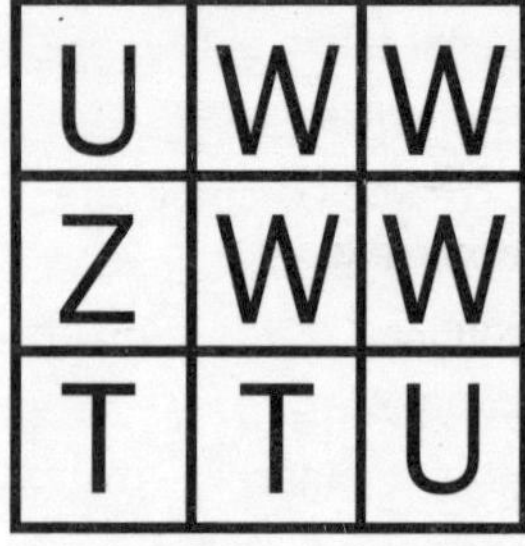

U	W	W
Z	W	W
T	T	U

The pattern sequence is:

ZRTTUWWZZS

Start at the bottom right and work up in a horizontal boustrophedon.

Puzzle 31

B.

Puzzle 32

48. In each box of four numbers, multiply the top two numbers, put the product in the bottom right box, then subtract the top right number from the bottom right one and put the difference in the bottom left box.

Puzzle 33

Independence. The initials can be rearranged to form the name Madrid.

Puzzle 34

No. She hates capital cities.

Puzzle 35

Gallus, Jovian, Julian, Trajan, Valens.

Puzzle 36

The pattern is:

+ + − − − ÷ ÷ x x x

Start at the top left and work clockwise in an inward spiral.

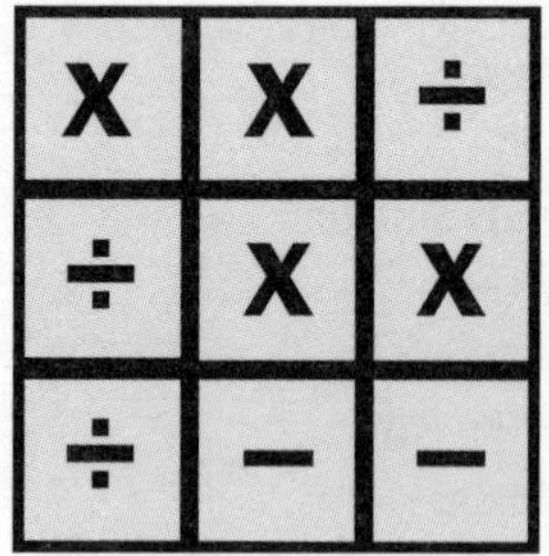

x	x	÷
÷	x	x
÷	−	−

Puzzle 37

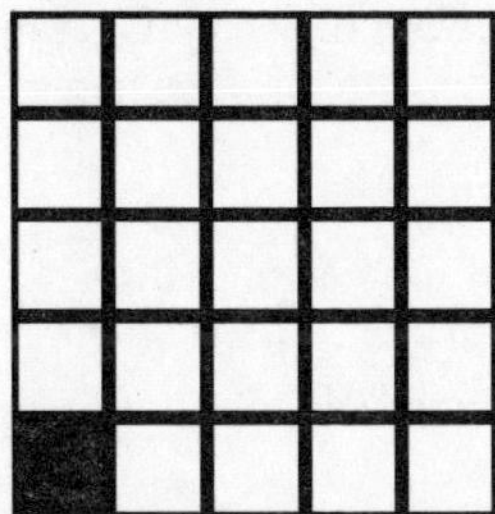

The shaded square moves around the square in a horizontal boustrophedon, starting at the top left hand corner. It advances by 2 squares, then 3, then 4, etc.

Puzzle 38

3. The numbers rotate anti-clockwise from one square to the next and decrease by 2 each time.

Puzzle 39

43.

Puzzle 40

1 White.
2 Chinese chess.
3 Pontoon.
4 The shape of the ball.
5 Mohammad Ali.
6 Draughts or checkers.
7 Chess.
8 Billiards.
9 Poker.
10 Cricket.
11 Ten-pin bowling.
12 Baseball.
13 A gridiron.
14 Jai alai or pelota.
15 Judo.
16 40.
17 A scrum.
18 True.
19 Lacrosse.
20 Ice hockey.
21 The sin bin.
22 Basketball.
23 Seven.
24 Volleyball.
25 Baseball.
26 No, only wooden ones.
27 Toe and heel plates screwed to the soles of their boots.
28 An over.
29 Willow.
30 Real tennis.
31 Tennis.
32 The 19th century.
33 None.
34 Table tennis.
35 Yes.
36 The speed of the ball.
37 Golf.
38 Soccer.
39 Angling.

40 The Olympics.

41 Poker.

42 Roulette.

43 Boules.

44 Hurling.

45 Curling.

46 Mah jongg.

47 Gin rummy.

48 Scrabble.

49 The crossword.

50 Marathon.

Puzzle 41

10. Add 2 to each value, place sum in corresponding position in next triangle, then subtract 3, add 2 again.

Puzzle 43

Blake, Byron, Dante, Donne, Plath.

Puzzle 44

E. Fold the top half onto the bottom half and turn the shape 45° anti-clockwise.

Puzzle 45

E. All the others contain two stars for every half moon.

Puzzle 42

A	R	C	D	E	T	R	I	O	M	P	A	R	C	D	E
R	R	R	T	E	D	C	R	A	H	P	M	O	I	R	T
C	D	C	T	R	I	O	M	P	H	E	H	P	M	O	I
D	E	T	D	E	T	R	I	O	M	A	R	C	D	E	A
H	P	M	O	I	R	T	E	D	P	M	O	I	R	T	R
A	R	C	D	E	T	R	I	E	O	M	P	H	E	A	R
C	R	A	E	H	P	M	T	E	D	I	R	T	E	D	C
D	E	T	R	I	O	R	M	P	H	C	E	A	R	C	D
C	D	T	R	I	I	O	M	P	H	E	R	M	I	I	E
R	A	E	H	O	P	M	O	I	R	T	P	A	R	R	T
O	M	P	M	H	E	A	R	I	D	E	H	O	T	T	R
I	R	P	T	E	D	C	R	A	E	H	E	I	E	E	I
R	H	C	D	E	T	R	I	O	M	P	A	R	D	D	O
E	A	H	P	M	O	I	R	T	E	D	R	T	A	C	M
D	E	T	R	I	O	M	P	H	A	R	C	E	R	R	P
C	R	A	H	P	M	O	I	R	T	E	D	D	C	A	H

Puzzle 46

S	T	A	T	U	E	O	R	T	S	T	A	T	U	E	S
S	R	E	B	I	L	F	O	E	U	T	A	T	A	T	D
L	S	T	A	T	U	L	I	B	E	R	T	O	F	F	A
I	L	I	B	E	R	T	E	L	I	B	E	R	L	O	T
B	O	F	L	I	B	U	E	O	S	T	A	I	F	S	U
E	T	S	T	A	T	U	E	O	F	S	B	T	S	O	F
R	O	F	L	A	S	U	F	T	L	E	T	T	A	S	L
T	I	C	T	B	T	L	R	I	T	Y	A	S	T	T	I
Y	U	S	E	A	I	S	B	Y	T	T	A	T	U	A	B
E	L	I	T	B	B	E	E	S	T	A	T	U	E	T	E
R	T	S	E	Y	R	Y	T	R	E	B	L	F	O	U	R
S	T	R	A	T	U	S	O	F	L	I	B	E	R	T	Y
L	T	I	S	B	E	T	O	F	S	T	A	T	U	E	O
Y	T	A	T	U	E	A	F	O	T	R	E	B	I	L	F
E	B	I	L	F	O	T	S	T	A	T	U	E	O	E	L
R	T	S	T	A	T	U	T	S	F	O	T	R	E	B	I

Puzzle 47

18. These are all the numbers that can be divided by either 3 or 4.

Puzzle 48

1956. The numbers represent the leap years clockwise around the triangles starting at the apex. Miss one leap year each time.

Puzzle 49

F. This is based on the number alphabet backwards. Add together the corner squares of each row or column and put the sum in the middle square of the opposite row or column.

Puzzle 50

Puzzle 51

R. Starting on the top left hand corner, work through the alphabet, missing a letter each time, in a vertical boustrophedon.

Puzzle 52

D. Add consecutive clockwise corners of the diamond and place the sum on the corresponding second corner. Add the four numbers together and place the sum in the middle.

Puzzle 53

1 Fort Knox in Kentucky.

2 Minting.

3 In the kingdom of Lydia, which is now known as Turkey.

4 The zloty.

5 Susan B. Anthony, a feminist leader.

6 Albania.

7 The thaler.

8 1971.

9 The dirham.

10 The Isle of Man, and the Channel Islands of Guernsey and Jersey.

11 Monte Carlo.

12 It was a silver coin used in Ancient Greece.

13 100 pfennig.

14 Numismatics.

15 Gold.

16 France.

17 The copper cent.

18 Twelve.

19 Tobacco leaves.

20 Sweden.

21 The forint.

22 The centime.

23 Intaglio plates.

24 China.

25 As dust.

26 The rupee.

27 Assignats.

28 The guinea.

29 They all use the peso.

30 The rand.

31 The Spanish conquerors of the Americas.

32 A female head representing the republic. It is popularly known as 'Marianne'.

33 The krona.

34 A farthing.

35 Japan.

36 Finland, which had a system that was introduced by the Russians and now uses the Euro.

37 The Ancient Greeks.

38 In Spain and Spanish America.

39 Copper plate money, from Sweden.

40 Venice.

41 A portrait of the emperor.

42 Copper, in the form of lumps.

43 In northern Italy.

44 There were two types of coin issued, one with French writing and one with Flemish writing.

45 Denmark, Sweden, and Norway.

46 The lira.

47 Telephone coins.

48 Cent.

49 Barter.

50 Krugerrands.

Puzzle 54

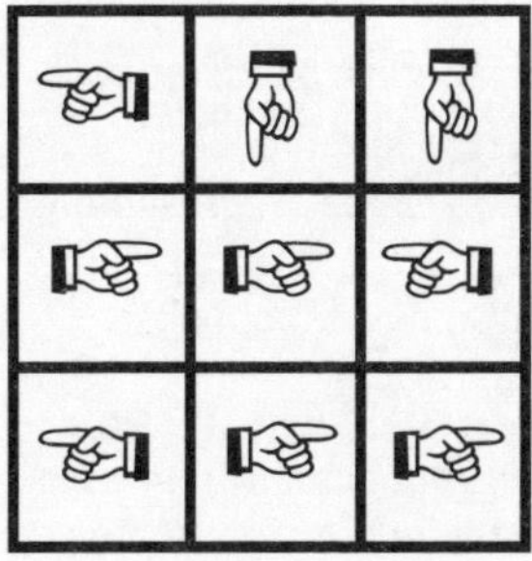

The pattern sequence is shown above. Starting at the bottom right, work in a diagonal boustrophedon (clockwise start).

Puzzle 55

C and **F**.

Puzzle 56

A Midsummer Night's Dream by William Shakespeare.

Puzzle 57

20. Left hand x right hand ÷ waist = head. Left foot x right foot ÷ waist = head.

Puzzle 59

Y. It spells Aldous Huxley.

Puzzle 60

83. Add the values of the letters in each box, based on the alphabet backwards (i.e. Z = 1, a = 26) and place the sum, with the digits reversed, two squares ahead.

Puzzle 58

The starting point is at Row 3 Col 9. The hidden number is 100.

W8
N3
SW2
S2
SW4

W5	NW4	E4
N1		NE2
E2		N2
S2		S2
W1	S4	S1

NE4	NW1	N2
N1		N3
E2		NE2
E6		SE2
S4	SE1	S1

Puzzle 61

She rubbed poison on one side of the knife blade.

Puzzle 62

4. Add the two top outer numbers from the upper boxes and the two bottom numbers from the lower boxes and put the sum in the inner box diagonally opposite. The third outer number is obtained by subtracting 3, 4, 5, and 6 from the adjoining answer, starting from the top left and reading clockwise. The answer is obtained as follows: 6 + 4 (top right's two outer top numbers) = 10 (bottom left's inner numbers) – 6 = 4.

Puzzle 63

Row 1, Col 1. The last letter represents the number of steps you have to go, based on the alphabet backward, however with Y = 1, X = 2, W = 3, A = 25, Z = 26. Start at the finishing point and work back.

Puzzle 64

D. An anti-clockwise spiral points up or left, a clockwise spiral down or right. A round shape has a small shape with straight lines attached, a straight-sided shape has a small shape with round lines attached to it.

Puzzle 65

The hidden letter is X, and the pattern is a vertical boustrophedon starting from the bottom left.

Puzzle 66

1 You thought Salome? No, she is not actually named in the Bible; the story comes from the ancient historian Josephus.

2 None of them was more than 5 ft tall.

3 Both members of a mating pair are hermaphrodite.

4 They did not rust.

5 Over 25,000.

6 It took place after he was dead.

7 Listening to 'The Lone Ranger' on the radio.

8 Joan of Arc.

9 The Boston Strangler.

10 Chattanooga, Tennessee.

11 Oregon.

12 Seventy.

13 Elhanan (II Samuel 21:19).

14 His body was stolen from the grave and held to ransom.

15 The Moon. Li Po was drunk and, while trying to kiss the reflection of the Moon, fell into the water and drowned.

16 They were all reported dead while still alive.

17 Nylon.

18 All studied for holy orders.

19 An apple.

20 They were all believers in astrology.

21 They were Green, Berry, and Hill.

22 They all played American Football.

23 Every 12 days.

24 'Peccavi', which in Latin means 'I have sinned'.

25 Charlie Chaplin.

26 One of three actors who played ET in scenes when a puppet was not used.

27 A dislike of punctuation.

28 They all went bankrupt at some stage in their careers.

29 They each had a sexual relationship with Aristotle Onassis.

30 They all committed incest.

31 The first ever kiss in an Indian film.

32 They were all married.

33 They were rejected 20 or more times before being published.

34 They each wrote one novel.

35 An old Persian measure of length.

36 Wear it: it is a man's short cloak.

37 Probably spend it: it is a reward.

38 A rehoboam.

39 A stew of green indian corn, beans and, if you're lucky, pork.

40 Throw it: it is a stick for throwing.

41 Continual means 'continuing but with interruptions'; continuous means 'continuing without interruption'.

42 They both had affairs at a very early age.

43 They were both created by someone called Edgar.

44 They were all left-handed.

45 They all went over the Niagara Falls in a barrel.

46 A pretty girl.

47 They all started out as trademarks.

48 They were all noted cat lovers.

49 Abnormal sensitivity to pain.

50 An alloy of copper with tin or zinc, used to imitate gold.

Puzzle 67
Columbus, Honolulu, Portland, San Diego, Syracuse.

Puzzle 68
The hidden letter is **F.** The pattern runs in diagonal stripes starting from the top right and going up from right to left.

Puzzle 69
B and **F**.

Puzzle 70
C. It spells Henri Toulouse-Lautrec.

Puzzle 71
D and **E**.

Puzzle 72
3. Each letter has a partner in the other triangle, which is its value in the alphabet backwards (A = 26, Z = 1). The number equivalent for C should be 24 (the letter for 3 is X).

Puzzle 73
A chest of drawers.

Puzzle 74
27. The numbers increase by 3, 4, 5, 6 in an anti-clockwise direction.

Puzzle 75
K. Add the values (based on the alphabet forward) of the letters, convert their value into a new letter (based on the alphabet backward) and put it two squares ahead.

Puzzle 76
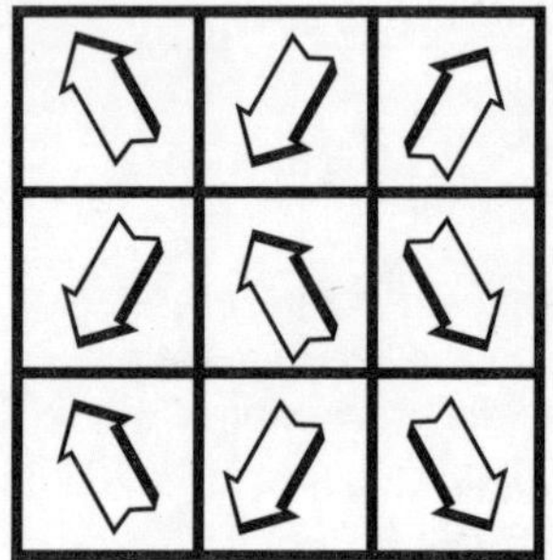

The pattern sequence is as above. It starts at the bottom right and works up in a horizontal boustrophedon.

Puzzle 77

Add the limbs of the figures on the outside of each segment and put the new figure, minus one limb into the middle two segments before.

Puzzle 78

He was captain of a ferry. The globe he went round was a decorative one he had in his cabin.

Puzzle 79

1 Never despair.

2 District of Columbia.

3 Tropic of Cancer.

4 Anti-clockwise.

5 Grass.

6 Nine-tenths.

7 The Marianas Trench.

8 Red dust blown up from the Sahara by the sirocco.

9 True. The Kerosene fungus (Amorpotheca resinae) can extract carbon from fuel and turn it into carbohydrate.

10 The smallest amount needed to kill a guinea pig weighing 250g (9oz) within four days.

11 Longsightedness.

12 The touch receptors on the tongue are 100 times denser than those on the back.

13 20%.

14 True.

15 1924.

16 New Zealand, in 1893.

17 The Maid of Zaragoza.

18 Colonel Blood.

19 Using the same letter or syllable several times in rapid succession (e.g., 'He is bearded, balding, but basically benevolent').

20 Dentine.

21 A reading desk.

22 Bronze – a mixture of copper and tin.

23 Because helium is much lighter than air.

24 The smallest part of any substance that can exist and yet still exhibit all the chemical properties of the substance.

25 Because the container of the vacuum gives off tiny traces of vapour which destroy the vacuum.

26 Because it combines with the haemoglobin in blood thus eliminating oxygen.

27 The main source of ore in a region.

28 A shrub of north-west North America, having white flowers and a dark purple, edible fruit.

29 A Native American food prepared from dried strips of meat pounded into a paste, mixed with fat and berries, and pressed into small cakes.

30 The honey bear.

31 Old Glory.

32 Oliver Cromwell.

33 Nibelung.

34 Brunhild.

35 Troika.

36 A large bus.

37 A frame slung between trailing poles and pulled by a dog or horse, formerly used by Plains Indians as a conveyance for goods and belongings.

38 Adolf Hitler.

39 He was martyred.

40 Lambarene.

41 The Dalai Lama.

42 One of a pair of metal supports used for holding up logs in a fireplace.

43 A surgical instrument having circular, saw-like edges, used to cut out disks of bone, usually from the skull.

44 In the atmosphere, above the troposphere and below the mesosphere.

45 A proof taken from composed type to allow for the correction of errors.

46 The last car on a freight train, having kitchen and sleeping facilities for the train crew.

47 John Calvin.

48 He advocated higher education for women and endowed Vassar College.

49 He was a candle maker.

50 Thomas Mann.

Puzzle 80

See opposite

Puzzle 81

Row 1, Column 1. The last letter is based on the alphabet backwards, starting with Y = 1, X = 2, W = 3 ... A = 25, Z = 26. Its value represents the number of spaces you have to move.

Puzzle 80

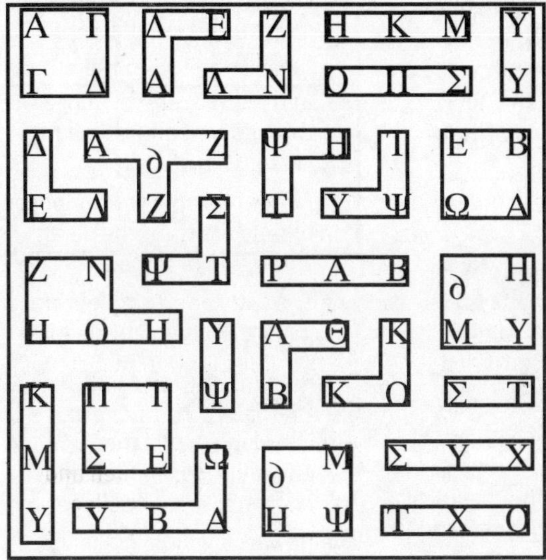

Puzzle 82

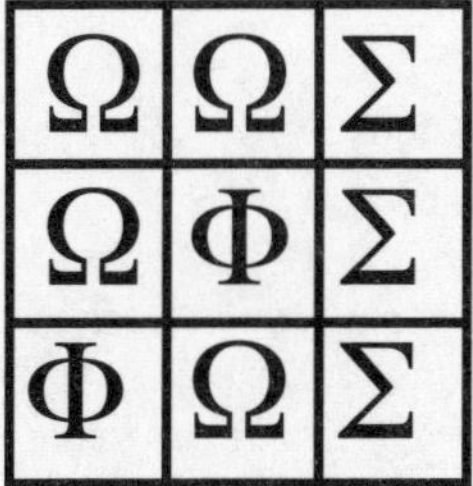

The pattern sequence is:

Φ Σ Σ Ω Ω Ω Σ Σ Φ

It starts at the bottom right and works up in a diagonal boustrophedon.

Puzzle 83

Their mother had produced triplets. However, being poor she had been unable to bring them all up and had given one up for adoption. Nevertheless, the family resemblance was so strong that the men recognized their long lost brother.

Puzzle 84

A and **N**. The series is B, D, F, H, J (2, 4, 6, 8, 10). Add 1, 2, 3, 4, 5 respectively to the values to get the letters in the second triangle.

Puzzle 85

10. Multiply the two numbers on the outside of each segment, divide the product by 1,2,3 ...8 respectively and put the new number in the middle of the opposite segment.

Puzzle 86

410. In all the others the first two digits added result in the third digit.

Puzzle 87

11. Multiply the number of sides of each number by 3, and then subtract the number printed.

Puzzle 88

Between the 4 and 5. When the numbers the two hands point to on each of the clocks are multiplied, the product is 36. $4\frac{1}{2} \times 8 = 36$.

Puzzle 89

B. Based on the values of the letters in the alphabet (Z = 1, A = 26), take the first and last letter of the make of the car.

Puzzle 90

		2
9		7
4	8	3

Puzzle 91

D. The symbols turn by 180° and 90° alternately. The circle and square swap places, the diamond and rectangle swap shading.

Puzzle 92

1 (a) Eastern prince.
2 (c) sooty.
3 (b) defamation.
4 (c) gourd.
5 (a) pregnant.
6 (b) part of a church.
7 (c) sickness.
8 (a) opera text.
9 (b) howling.
10 (c) flower ovary.
11 (b) hat.
12 (b) hidden.
13 (c) humped.
14 (b) flash.
15 (b) temporary ban.

16 (a) blink.
17 (b) artificial body part.
18 (b) deputy.
19 (b) marsh.
20 (c) cell division.
21 (b) bombastic.
22 (c) scaly.
23 (a) gewgaw.
24 (b) tearful.
25 (c) describe.
26 (b) powerless.
27 (a) ring-shaped.
28 (b) frenzied.
29 (c) fabric.
30 (a) fibre.
31 (a) change shape.
32 (c) dim.
33 (a) uninteresting.
34 (b) imperfectly formed.
35 (b) yaws.
36 (a) spirochetes.
37 (b) metallic element.
38 (b) burn suddenly.
39 (a) wandering.
40 (b) tax.
41 (a) style of music.
42 (b) wheelbarrow.
43 (a) piddock.
44 (b) asking.
45 (a) tallness.
46 (a) heifer.
47 (b) to constrain.
48 (b) flower part.
49 (a) everywhere.
50 (a) canto.

NOTES